S0-BEW-283

# Man the Astronomer

*Frontispiece* A spiral galaxy in Andromeda, photographed with 24-in reflector, Yerkes Observatory, 1901. (overleaf)

# Man the Astronomer

Patrick Moore OBE
Director of the Lunar Section
of the Royal Astronomical Society

Scottdale Public Library
Founded 1910

520.9
M

PRIORY PRESS LIMITED

## *Social History of Science Library*

**Man the Astronomer** Patrick Moore
**Man the Aviator** Charles Harvard Gibbs-Smith
**Man the Builder** John Harvey
**Man the Explorer** G R Crone
**Man the Farmer** Robert Trow-Smith
**Man the Navigator** Wing-Commander E W Anderson
**Man and the Wheel** B S Benson
**Man the Industrialist** Peter Hobday
**Man the Healer** W R Trotter
**Man the Toolmaker** Michael Grey
**Man and Measurement** Keith Ellis
**Man and his Money** Keith Ellis
**Man the Shipbuilder** Maurice Griffiths
**Man the Steelmaker** W K V Gale

SBN 85078 137 X
Copyright © 1973 by Patrick Moore
First Published in 1973 by
Priory Press Ltd
Text set in Baskerville
and printed in Great Britain by
Page Bros (Norwich) Ltd, Norwich

# Contents

# *List of Illustrations*

# *Acknowledgements*

The author's and publishers' thanks are due to Lawrence Clarke, for his skilful drawings.

# *Picture Credits*

The author and publishers wish to thank the following for permission to reproduce copyright illustrations on the pages mentioned: NASA, 106, 114; Radio Times Hulton Picture Library, 19, 30, 46–47, 65, 68, 102 (bottom); Ronan Picture Library, 16, 17, 22, 23, 24, 26, 28, 33, 37, 38, 41, 43, 47, 49, 51, 52, 53, 55, 56, 59, 74, 78, 85, 93, 94, 95, 100 (bottom), 101; Royal Astronomical Society, 89, 100 (top); Science Museum, *frontispiece*, 64, 69, 70, 71, 75, 81, 82, 90; United Press Agency, 103, 104.

## CHAPTER ONE

# *Man and the Sky*

Look up into the sky on a dark, clear night, and you will see stars. You may well imagine that these stars are to be numbered in their millions, and it comes as something of a shock to learn that nobody can ever see as many as four thousand stars at any one time—unless, of course, optical aid is used. With the help of a telescope, the number of visible stars really does run into millions; but the telescope is a relatively modern invention, dating back less than four centuries. Ancient races had to rely solely upon their eyes.

A casual glance is enough to show that the stars are not all of the same brightness, and slightly more careful examination shows that they are not all of the same colour. Most are white, but a few are perceptibly orange or orange-red. Then, too, there are some objects which are exceptionally brilliant, and seem to be of a different nature from the run-of-the-mill stars.

Our remote ancestors could notice this, too; and undoubtedly they did so. Yet they could have no idea of the scale of the universe, and to them the Earth seemed to be a flat plane, lying motionless with the entire sky revolving round it once a day. This was a perfectly reasonable picture, and in fact anything else would have been illogical. Surely the stars, the Sun, the Moon, and the sky itself

Prais'd be the fathomless
universe
For life and joy, and for
objects and knowledge
curious.

WALT WHITMAN

Speech created thought,
Which is the measure of the
Universe.

SHELLEY

I don't pretend to understand the Universe—it's a great deal bigger than I am . . . People ought to be modester.

CARLYLE

must have been made specially for the benefit of mankind?

We have come a long way from those far-off days, and the more we have learned the less important we believe ourselves to be. But astronomy—the study of the skies—has practical applications too, and these have been very much to the fore in recent years. Many centuries ago, in Ancient Egypt, it was the astronomers who watched the rising of the bright star Sirius and warned the farmers that they might expect the Nile to flood at any moment. The modern astronomer is concerned with communications, with physics, even with medical research and many other branches of science, as well as with the study of the stars.

This is not a book about astronomy as a science. What I hope to do is to trace the story of how astronomy has affected the attitude of men throughout the ages. The story has several well-defined chapters, and there have been some unfortunate episodes; it is rather difficult nowadays to credit that as recently as 1600 one scientist was burned at the stake because he persisted in teaching that the Earth moves round the Sun instead of vice versa. (His name was Giordano Bruno. To be accurate, this was only one of his many crimes in the opinion of the Christian Church, and probably not the most serious of them; but his defence of a moving Earth certainly contributed to his being sentenced to death.)

So let us first look back in time as far as we can—to the period before written records existed, and before civilization began. The essential point to be borne in mind here is that the skies looked much the same then as they do now. If we could equip ourselves with a time machine—Dr. Who's *Tardis* would do nicely—and project ourselves back to, say, the year 20,000 BC, the star-patterns would not be very different from those we know today. Over a lifetime, or even over a hundred lifetimes, the patterns do not alter perceptibly. Naturally, ancient peoples believed that the stars were fixed, probably to a solid vault; and the expression "fixed stars" is still quite common. Strictly speaking it is incorrect, because the stars are not fixed in space. They are suns, many of them far larger, hotter and more powerful than our own Sun; and they are moving about very quickly in all sorts of directions. Their individual movements do not show up for the simple reason that they are a very long way away from us. Even the nearest star, not counting the Sun, lies at a distance of well over twenty million million miles.

Primitive man must, of course, have noticed that the stars seem to move round the Earth, completing one circuit in a period equal to about twenty-four of our modern hours. Some of the stars were always on view; dwellers in Ancient Britain could always see the seven stars of the group we now call the Great Bear. Others were visible only at definite seasons of the year. The Sun, too, took part in this general rotation—as did the Moon. The only difference was that the Moon, at least, shifted about among the star-groups, and presumably the same applied to the Sun, though the brightness of the daytime sky made it impossible to see the Sun and the stars at the same time. During summer, the Sun rose high in the sky; during winter its altitude was less.

Every modern schoolboy knows the reason for this behaviour. The Earth is a planet—that is to say a non-luminous globe, moving round the Sun; it completes one journey in a period of a year, and in addition it is spinning on its axis, turning once in 24 hours. The apparent rotation of the sky is due to the real rotation of the Earth. The axis points northward to a position we call the north

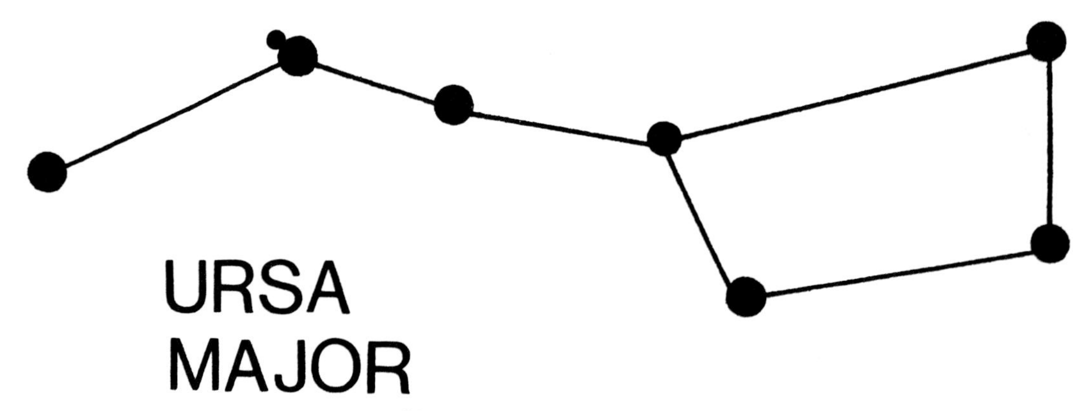

# URSA MAJOR

Ursa Major, the Great Bear

celestial pole, marked nowadays by a bright star, Polaris (though at the start of written history the pole was in a different place, and there was a different pole star.) The seasons are due to the tilt of the Earth's axis; during northern summer the north pole is tipped toward the Sun, and we in Britain receive the maximum benefit from the solar rays. Nothing could be more straightforward —but to the cave-men of so long ago the situation was very much less clear-cut.

Remember, there is no way of estimating the distance of a star, or the Sun or Moon, simply by looking at it. One cannot tell immediately that the Moon is nearer than the stars, or that some stars are more remote than others. The idea of a solid "vault of heaven" may sound absurd to us, but to early races it was natural. Also, how can one tell from superficial observation that the Earth is shaped like a globe rather than a pancake?

Quite apart from all this, there was the original, perfectly sensible idea that Man must be unique, and that the entire universe (whatever it might be) had been created for his sole benefit. The Sun was there to provide light and heat during the daytime, and at night the Moon provided at least a reasonable amount of illumination. In some places, at least, the phase of the Moon must have been an important consideration. Dark nights were the most dangerous ones, since intense blackness provided a cover for treacherous attacks on settlements and even strongholds. However, the dark periods could be predicted, since the Moon behaved in a perfectly regular and predictable manner, and suitable precautions could be taken. This was where the early astronomers proved so useful. Their studies of the sky had a very practical value, and unquestionably they were regarded as "wise men" in the best sense of the term.

It is often said that astronomy is the oldest science in the world. This may well be true, but the statement needs qualifying. First, we have no idea of when it began, because it was already in existence when the first records were kept; we may surely assume that the skies were observed even by the half-men who roamed the world during the Ice Age. Secondly, it can hardly be said that this sort of observation was real "astronomy". The old star-gazers had no conception of the plan of the universe, and we cannot even be certain that they were sufficiently advanced mentally to be interested. Only when modern-type man came into existence can we really claim that conscious astronomy started; and even then it was remarkably limited.

It was also coupled with religion, since there was every reason to think that the Sun and Moon were either gods or at least the abodes of gods. Now and then, too, terrifying things happened; there were even moments when the Sun seemed to be blotted out during broad daylight, so that presumably it must be under attack by some devil or dragon. Certainly there was much to be learned, and much to be feared.

How long did this period last? We cannot tell,

because there is still considerable disagreement as to the time when modern-type man made his entry. We do know, however, that it ended around five thousand years ago. It was then that we see the start of true science, and this, predictably, had tremendous effects upon the whole outlook of mankind.

## CHAPTER TWO

# *Gods and Calendars*

Any man—ancient or modern—is apt to exaggerate the importance of his home. To people living in, say, the Outer Hebrides, the small town of Stornoway looms much larger than distant London or even more distant New York. My own home is in Selsey, on the coast of Sussex; the nearest towns of moderate size are Chichester and Bognor Regis, and I think much more often about them, than about Los Angeles or San Francisco. Small wonder, then, that early peoples regarded their own particular countries as all-important; and in our survey of attitudes during historical times it will be best to begin with Egypt, because the outlook of their "wise men" was so typical and so natural.

We of today know that Egypt makes up part of the vast continent of Africa. The Pyramid-builders of several thousand years BC did not know this, and could not have credited it. To them Egypt herself was supreme, and lay in the middle of the Earth, surrounded on all sides by a huge ocean. The Earth itself was flat, and the whole universe took the form of a rectangular box, with the longer sides running north-south. Above the Earth there was a ceiling, supported by four pillars at the cardinal points; the pillars were connected by a mountain chain, and below this chain lay a ledge

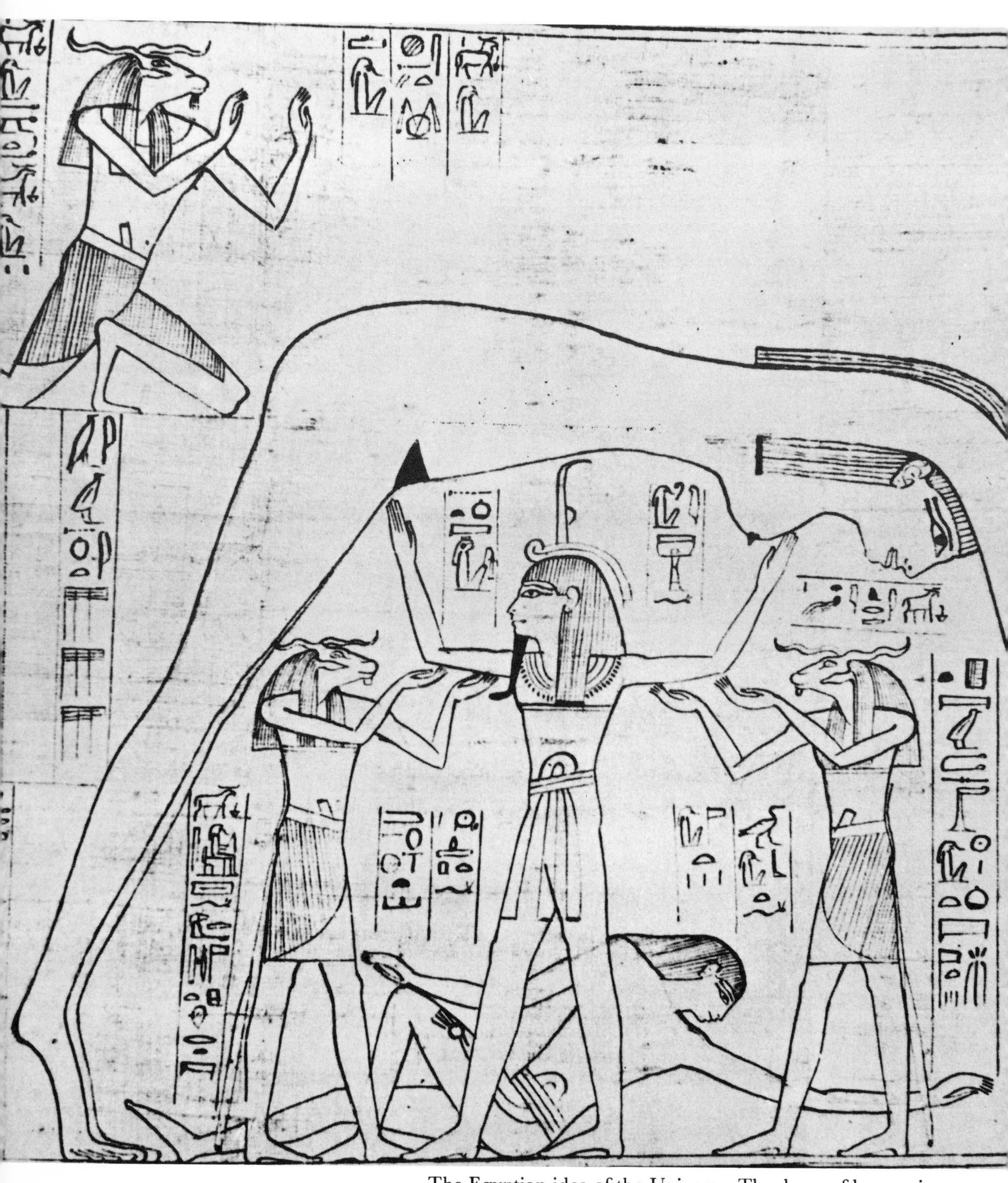

The Egyptian idea of the Universe. The dome of heaven is represented by the body of the Sky-goddess, Nut, who is supported by the god Thoth. The reclining figure represents the Earth-god Queb. From a funerary papyrus about BC 970

carrying the celestial river Ur-nes. Boats carrying the Sun, the Moon and other gods sailed along this river, and people of the eastern cities of the Nile Delta even believed that the heavens were formed by the body of the goddess Nut. They also considered that the celestial bodies moved round the Earth in square paths, so that when the Sun or Moon happened to come to a corner it turned sharply at right angles.

Clearly there is no science in this sort of belief, and it is not easy to understand how some of the wilder ideas can have originated; but we must always remember that they were drawn up and taught by comparatively few people—mainly the priests, whose authority was tremendous. Ordinary folk simply accepted the picture, if indeed they thought about it at all, and their studies of the sky were confined merely to looking up at it. Interpretation was not their concern; this was best left to the priestly leaders. Obviously this suited the priests very well. They were regarded as a superior class, and their teachings were never questioned.

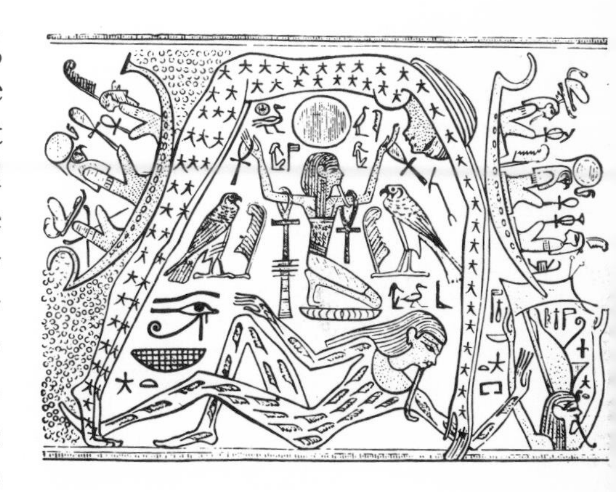

The Egyptian cosmos.

Moreover, Egyptian religion was bound up with the bodies of the sky—who has not heard of Ra, the Sun-God? In laying down the law about what could be seen in the sky, the priests were also claiming insight into the divine forces which ruled all humanity (which, to them, meant all Egypt). To cast doubt upon the authority of men such as this would, presumably, have been regarded as highly dangerous. There is every reason to think that the people as a whole simply accepted what they were told by their masters, and that they had a comfortable feeling of being specially protected.

This was one part of the story; but there was another. The priest-astronomers were practical as well as power-conscious, and in some respects their advice was needed. The Egypt of those days was entirely dependent upon its farming, and this in turn was controlled by one river: the Nile. Each year there came the great flooding, and it was essential to know just when this might be expected. This meant the drawing-up of a calendar, which could be based upon nothing but astronomy, and which was fixed eventually at 365 days. Of course, even the priests had no idea that the year was simply the time taken for the Earth to go round the Sun, and from a purely practical point of view the cause was unimportant. One excellent method of making a time-check was to watch for what was called the "heliacal rising" of the star Sirius—that is to say the period each year when Sirius could first be seen in the sky just before dawn. Sirius is much the brightest star in the heavens, and could always be identified.

This raises another interesting point. Brilliant though Sirius may be, it is not nearly so striking as some of the planets—Venus, Mars and Jupiter. But the planets move around among the constellations, and their "heliacal risings" are not the same each year, so that for time-checking purposes they were useless. Obviously the priests knew this, and also knew that Sirius does not change its position, relative to the other stars, even over very long periods. It seems, then, that they must have realized that the planets are different in nature from the stars.

There is another proof that despite their complete ignorance about the universe (or even about the status of the Earth), the Egyptians were skilful observers. The famous Pyramids were astronomically aligned. These immense structures still stand; there have been endless discussions as to how they were actually built, and scholars still argue about their exact rôle in Egyptian life and death—but of their importance there can be no doubt at all. The Pyramid-building age was between 2000 and 3000 BC; in view of the fact that

The Great Pyramid of Cheops at Gaza

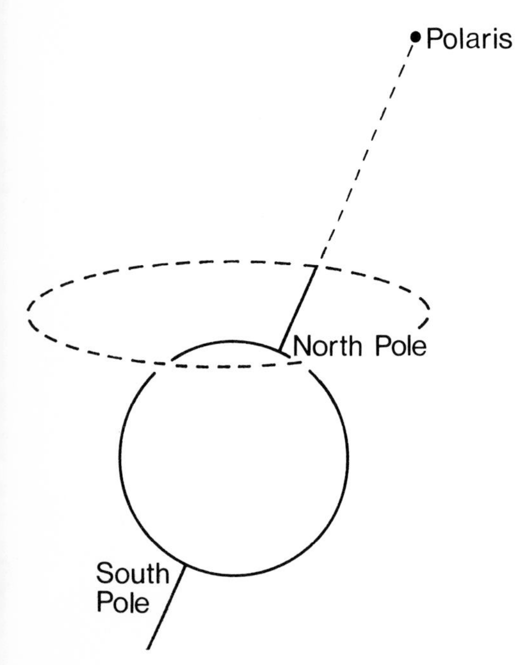


The direction of the Earth's axis. As shown by the dotted line, the axis changes slowly in direction; this is the cause of precession

everything had to be done by hand, the accuracy of their construction is amazing. With the Great Pyramid, the main passage was oriented with respect to the north pole of the sky, which was not in quite the same position as it is now. As we have seen, our present north polar star is Polaris, in the constellation which we call Ursa Minor, the Little Bear. In Pyramid-building times, the pole star was Thuban, a much less conspicuous star some way away. The shift is due to the phenomenon of precession.

There is no mystery about precession. As the Earth spins round, it is "wobbling" very slowly and very slightly, rather in the manner of a gyroscope which is running down and has started to topple. This means that the direction of the axis alters, making one full turn in a period of approximately 26,000 years. I shall have more to say about precession later, when we come to consider the cult of astrology; for the moment it is enough to say that it provides us with a very good means of checking the time at which the Pyramids were set up.

All in all, Egyptian astronomy was a curious mixture of careful, accurate observation and equally inaccurate, unscientific interpretation. The main thing to remember from a social point of view is that it was highly practical. Without it, agriculture would have been in a state of chaos, with disastrous results. Even today there are people who claim that astronomy is a purely academic study, of no real interest except to those who are anxious to collect knowledge for its own sake. This is not true; and neither was it true in Ancient Egypt.

Before leaving the land of the Pyramids, we must pause to consider one curious episode which has at least some sort of link with astronomy, and which for a brief period affected the life of the entire nation. In Egyptian religion there were many gods. Ra, in his various forms, was only one of them; another was Osiris, God of the Underworld. This was the accepted view in or about the year 1379 BC, when a young man named Amenophis became Pharaoh. At the start of his reign he was known as Amenophis IV, but before long he changed it to Akhenaten, and did his best to overthrow all the old-established religious ideas. He founded the cult of Sun-worship; there was only one god—the Sun-disk, or Aton—and the Pharaoh even moved his capital to a new city which he founded. In his religion love and happiness were all-important, and cruelty was outlawed. The whole of his glorious "Hymn to the Sun" has come down to us, and remains unique.

Inevitably the experiment failed. An idealist such as Akhenaten could not hope to rule a large, turbulent nation, particularly when the priesthood was hostile to him. The priests did not take kindly to the idea of having their supreme authority undermined; Akhenaten was overthrown, and before long his religion had been very efficiently wiped out. Nothing comparable has been attempted since.

We cannot tell what would have happened if, against all the odds, Akhenaten had succeeded in his plans. Historians will claim that Egypt's power would have crumbled away, and this is probably true—but Egyptian power decayed in any case, so that a change in religion might not have made so very much difference in the long run. And it may be argued that if the Egyptians had kept to Akhenaten's "religion of love" they might have made a greater contribution to human culture than they actually did. However, after so many centuries it is really rather pointless to speculate.

What we have said about the Egyptians applies

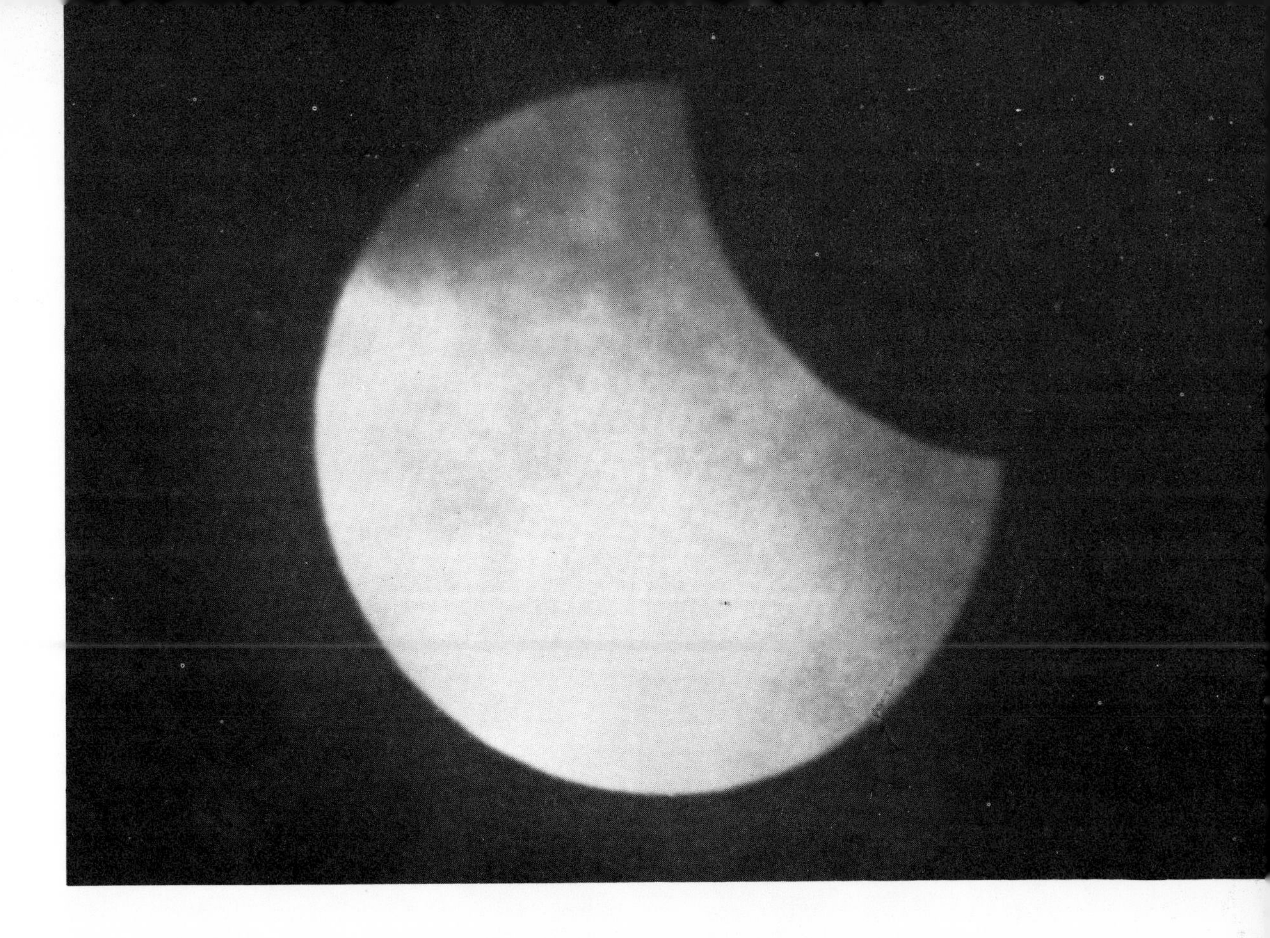

Partial solar eclipse, photographed in 1968. Note the interference from clouds. The photograph was taken by the author, using a 3-in. refracting telescope.

in much the same way to that other great civilization of ancient times: China. Here too there arose a class of "wise men" who claimed to have a deep knowledge of the sky, and hence of the gods who presumably lived there. As with Egypt, the question of a calender was important; and again it was the astronomers who provided it. Originally it was rather less accurate than the Egyptian, with a 360-day year, but it served its purpose fairly well. Here, too, the stars were divided into groups or constellations—though, needless to say, the Chinese constellations were different from the Egyptian, and both were different from those which we use today.

The Chinese astronomical records are full of interest, and they are also very useful in modern research, quaint though they are. There is one story which is worth re-telling, though its authenticity is very dubious. This concerns two Court

Akhenaten with his consort Nefertiti and their two daughters offering gifts to the Sun. This relief was originally in the Temple of the Sun at Thebes, which was destroyed after Akhenaten's death (*opposite*)

Total solar eclipse photographed on January 22 1898. The corona is clearly visible

astronomers with the rather unlikely names of Hi and Ho. The episode is said to date from 2136 BC, during the reign of the emperor Chung K'ang.

Among the events recorded by the Chinese were eclipses of the Sun. We know that they are due to the Moon, which passes in front of the Sun and may blot out the brilliant solar disk. During a partial eclipse it seems as though there is a "bite" out of the Sun; if the eclipse is total, there is a glorious, brief period (never as long as 8 minutes) when the Sun is hidden altogether, and the scene is dominated by the solar atmosphere, which seems to shine out all round the dark disk of the Moon.

This atmosphere—or, rather, that part of it which we call the corona—can be seen with the naked eye only during a total eclipse, though modern instruments make the inner part of it available for study at any time. The last total eclipse visible from any part of England occurred in 1927, and the next will not be until 1999, so that they are not commonplace even though other parts of the world have been more favoured.

With their primitive ideas about Nature, the Chinese had no thought that the Moon might be concerned, and they had a very different explanation. They believed that during an eclipse, a hungry dragon was doing its best to eat the Sun. Clearly this could not be allowed, and the obvious course was to make as much noise as humanly possible, so that the entire populace poured outdoors shouting, wailing, and beating gongs and drums. Invariably the dragon was scared off, and the Sun regained its light; but it was highly desirable to know when the attacks were due—and this was where the astronomers came in.

The Moon moves round the Earth,* taking just over 27 days to complete one journey. When it is approximately between us and the Sun, its dark or night side is turned toward us, and the Moon is new, it cannot normally be seen. If the alignment is exact, we have an eclipse. However, eclipses do not occur every month, because the Moon's path is somewhat tilted, and generally the new moon passes unnoticed either above or below the Sun in the sky. Because of the combined movements of Earth, Sun and Moon, it has been found that eclipses tend to recur after an interval of rather more than 18 years, a period known as the Saros.

The Chinese theory of a total eclipse—a dragon attacking the Sun!

* To be strictly accurate, the Earth and Moon revolve round their common centre of gravity; but in our present context this distinction is not important.

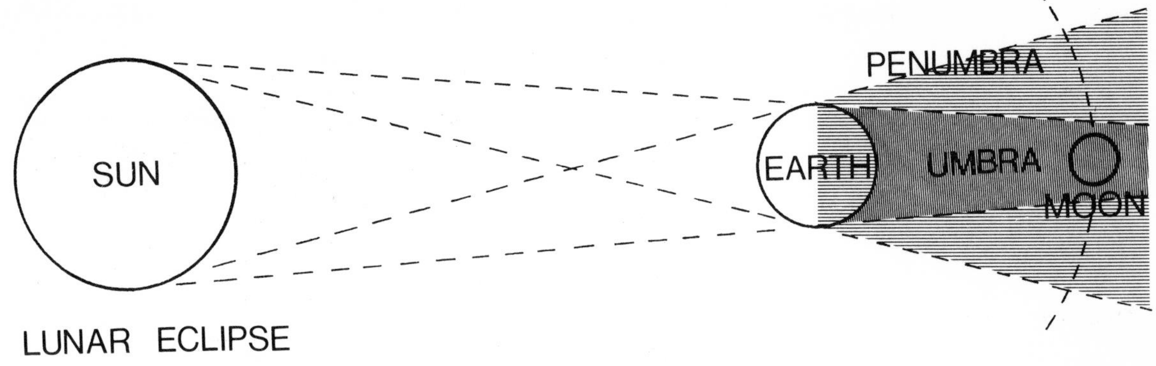


Orbits of the Moon

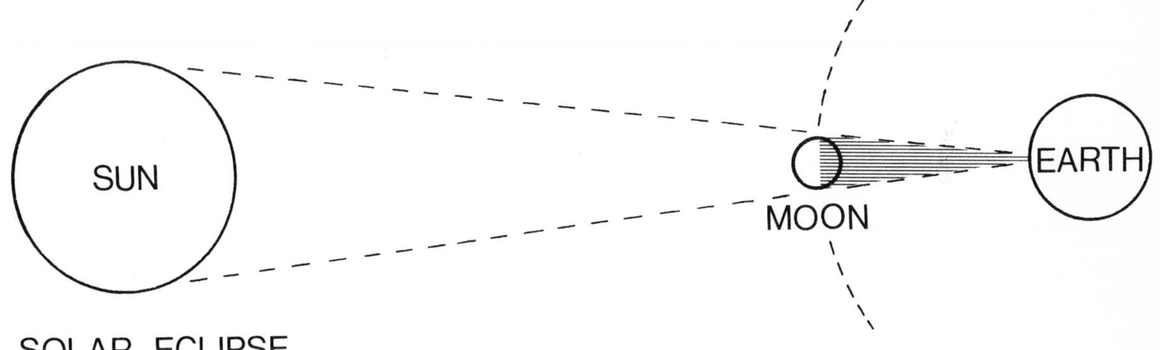


Theory of Lunar (above) and Solar (below) eclipses

This means that as a rough rule eclipses can be predicted by simple addition; one eclipse is likely to be followed by another one, 6585 days later.

This was the sort of thing which Chung K'ang's wise men were expected to know. Unfortunately Hi and Ho, holders of the office of Court Astronomers, were not on the alert, and they failed to predict the eclipse of 2136 BC, so that when the dragon began its attack the Imperial household was caught unawares. When the eclipse was over, and the dragon had withdrawn, Hi and Ho were summoned to the Emperor's presence, and summarily beheaded.

I have a feeling that this story comes into the same category as that of Canute and the waves; but it is not impossible, and it is quite definite that eclipses of the Sun caused the Chinese considerable

This picture from the *Illustrated London News,* shows the effect of the total solar eclipse in India in 1871 on the people of Bekul. These Indians are reacting as strongly as the Chinese did many centuries earlier *(opposite)*

The Comet of 1479 seen through the clouds. This picture was in a book published in Basle in 1557

alarm. Again we come back to the idea that the Earth is the supreme body in the universe, and that the skies are fashioned entirely for the benefit (or otherwise) of mankind.

Comets, too, were recorded in Old China. We know that a comet is a harmless body made up of small particles and thin gas; it moves round the Sun, and shines mainly by reflected sunlight. Admittedly a bright comet may have a long tail, and will appear imposing, but its mass is very small by astronomical standards. The fear of comets was only partly due to the possibility of a collision. It was believed that a comet was a sign of approaching disaster, and was sent by special order of the gods.

So much for Egypt and China. We need pause only briefly to mention some of the other bizarre theories of ancient times, fascinating though they are. To the Babylonians the sky was solid, so that each day the Sun entered through a door in the east and set every evening through another door in the west; the Hebrews believed the world to be supported on pillars, and to some of the peoples of Ancient India the Earth was said to be carried on the shoulders of elephants, while the elephants were in turn held up on the shell of a vast turtle swimming in a limitless sea. And to the Hindus, the Earth itself was the shape of a pyramid, sloping down from the plateau of Tibet to the Ganges Valley and down to the sea; on the top of the pyramid was Mount Meru, home of the gods, "golden and shining like the fire which is not dulled by smoke."

Meanwhile, what of Ancient Britain? Here, too, astronomy of a kind flourished rather more vigorously than was thought until recently. On Salisbury Plain there stands the famous stone circle of Stonehenge, now believed to have been built between 2800 and 1900 BC. Stand near the centre of the circle on Midsummer Day, and you will see the Sun rise over one particular stone beyond the circle. This Heel Stone is unquestionably a marker, and researches by the British scientist Gerald Hawkins seem to have established that Stonehenge was used by its makers to predict eclipses. Everything depends on the position of sunrise as seen from inside the main circle, and the accuracy seems too great to be explained away as a coincidence.

Unfortunately we know little about the Stonehenge-builders, because they left no written records—and, in passing, there is absolutely no connection with the Druids, who did not arrive in England until very much later. (In time, Stonehenge is as remote from the Druids as we are from Alfred the Great.) But as well as being a monument, it seems to have been nothing more nor less than a primitive computer, and this is enough to show that the people of Ancient Britain, too, were skilled observers.

With Egypt, China and Stonehenge we come almost to the end of our second period in astronomical history. Observation had been developed; theory lay in the future, at least from the scientific point of view. Stars were fixed to the solid vault of the sky, and the Sun and Moon, at least, were associated with the gods even if they were not themselves gods.

Astronomy was not purely academic. As we have seen, it was of immense practical value. Moreover, it was the Wise Men's knowledge of astronomy which gave them their immense authority, and placed them in a class above that of the ordinary people. Though ancient races in general knew nothing about the universe, they were in effect ruled by astronomy—by way of the priests. In fact, studies of the sky have had an exceptionally great social influence all through history.

Stonehenge

## CHAPTER THREE

# *Science and Prejudice*

The next period in our story is essentially Greek. It begins with the career of Thales of Miletus, who was born about 624 BC; it ends with that of Ptolemy of Alexandria, who died near AD 180. The period is of special importance for two reasons. It marked the first efforts at genuinely theoretical science, and—less creditably—it also saw the first example of scientific persecution (or, to be more cautious, the first example which is definitely known to us.)

Thales was undoubtedly a great philosopher. Many sayings are attributed to him, and one is worth quoting: "Of all things the most ancient is God, for he is uncreated; the most beautiful is the universe, for it is God's workmanship; the greatest is Space, for it contains everything; the swiftest is Mind, for it speeds everywhere; the strongest is Necessity, for it masters all; and the wisest is Time, for it brings everything to light." There are many modern writers who would be glad to have written this—though, let us add, we have no absolute proof that the words are Thales' own.

There is no doubt that he paid great attention to astronomy, and the tale that on one occasion he tumbled into a well while walking along gazing upward at the stars may well be true. Another story is almost certainly correct, though the date may be wrong—it is generally given as 28th May 585 BC. At that time a war was in progress between the Lydians and the Medes, and Thales had predicted an eclipse of the Sun, no doubt by the ancient method of using the Saros period (as Hi and Ho had so signally failed to do!). To quote the great writer Herodotus: "Just as the battle was growing warm, day was suddenly changed into night. When the Lydians and the Medes observed the change, they ceased fighting, and were anxious to conclude peace." This may well be the first occasion on which an astronomical event had a direct influence on the progress of a war, even though it was by no means the last.

Let us admit that Thales' successful prediction was decidedly lucky, because the Saros is not reliable so far as solar eclipses are concerned; the "return" of an eclipse one Saros later is often not visible from the same part of the Earth. On this occasion, however, the forecast was accurate, and Thales' reputation was made. Yet in many ways his ideas were no more advanced than those of the Pyramid-builders. He believed the Earth to be flat, and considered that it floated on water in the manner of a cork. Water was the most important of all substances; earth was condensed water; fire was simply heated air. Whether he made extensive observations of the stars we do not know, since none of his original writings survive.

This, as I have said, is not a book about the science of astronomy, and so it is not the place to go into any detail about Greek beliefs; but they cannot be entirely glossed over, because they have a tremendous influence on the general outlook of people of the time. Anaximenes, also of Miletus, lived from about 585 to 528 BC, and held that the Sun, Moon and stars originally came from Earth; the stars are made of fire that has risen aloft, and the Sun and Moon also are fiery, floating in the air

because of their flatness and their breadth. The stars are fixed on to an invisible crystal sphere, which turns round the world once a day.

Thales' concept of a flat earth floating on water. The central figure represents Archimedes. From Archimedes' *Tetragonismis,* printed in 1503 at Venice

Xenophanes, around 500 BC, maintained that the Sun is extinguished every night, so that a new Sun is created in time for the next dawn; Heraclitus of Ephesus considered that the Sun could be no more than twelve inches in diameter—and so on. It is quite wrong to suppose, as some people do, that Greek science blossomed rapidly. It did nothing of the kind. Yet here and there we come to a new and all-important idea, one of which was attributed (possibly rightly) to Pythagoras.

Pythagoras, born at Samos around 572 BC, seems to have thought that instead of being flat the Earth is spherical. It is also said that he knew about the independent movements of the planets against the starry background, though it would be very surprising to find that this was not known much earlier. He was, of course, a famous mathematician (who has not learned the famous Theorem of Pythagoras?) and he was also the centre of a widespread organization which began as a kind of religious brotherhood, and was eventually suppressed. He believed the soul of a man could pass from one body into another, and he stressed the need for leading a pure life—though many of his teachings sound like primitive tabus; for instance, it was forbidden to eat beans, or to poke a fire with an iron bar! This, needless to say, has nothing to do with astronomy, but Pythagoras' great influence gave his astronomical views an authority which they might not otherwise have had.

Next we come to the first act of deliberate persecution—and this cannot be passed over, because it set the pattern for much of what was to follow fifteen centuries later. It showed, too, that the attitude of at least some of the Greeks was not so very different from that of the dreaded Inquisition which brought Galileo to trial.

The victim was Anaxagoras, who was born

about 500 BC at Clazomenae, not far from Smyrna, but who soon moved to the cultural centre of the civilized world: Athens. When someone asked him the object of being born, he is said to have replied: "To investigate the Sun, the Moon and heaven." It is true that he believed the world to be flat, but he can certainly be described as a true scientist inasmuch as he observed as well as theorized. He knew that the Moon is not self-luminous, but shines by reflecting the light of the Sun; this led him on to a correct explanation of solar and lunar eclipses. Also, he was confident that life exists on other worlds as well as on the Earth. This was a revolutionary idea indeed, and was perhaps the first definite suggestion that the Earth is not the supreme body in the universe.

At this time the ruler of Athens was Pericles, who for a time held absolute power. Anaxagoras enjoyed his friendship, and was able to continue his studies in peace, but eventually—not long before the outbreak of the disastrous Peloponnesian War, which ended in defeat for Athens at the hands of Sparta—Pericles became unpopular. This rubbed off on Anaxagoras, and his enemies looked around for ways in which to attack him. They found an excuse in Anaxagoras' theory of the Sun, which he regarded as a red-hot stone larger than the Peloponnesus. Such an idea was said to be impious, and for a time the philosopher's life may have been in real danger. Pericles managed to save him; but he was compelled to leave Athens, and he retired to Lampsacus, where he remained until his death at the age of seventy-two.

Probably the onslaught on Anaxagoras was aimed not principally at him, but at Pericles. However, the end result was the same. For holding a perfectly reasonable scientific view, a great man was persecuted and banished. It is not easy to

Nature that fram'd us of
four elements
Warring within our breasts
for regiment
Doth teach us all to have
aspiring minds:
Our souls, whose faculties
can comprehend
The wondrous Architecture
of the world:
And measure every
wand'ring planets' course,
Still climbing after
knowledge infinite,
And always moving as the
restless Spheres,
Will us to wear ourselves
and never rest,
Until we reach the ripest
fruit of all,
*Conquests of Tamberlaine*,
MARLOWE

decide on the full facts of the case, but the spirit of intolerance and bigotry had reared its ugly head.

Not many decades later, Athens had cause to regret that the teachings of Anaxagoras had not been widely spread around. The Peloponnesian War raged, and Athens lost it very largely because of an eclipse of the Moon.

The struggle between the Athenians and the Spartans was at its height in the year 413 BC. Rather unwisely, the Athenians had sent a major expedition to the island of Sicily, and had entrusted the command to one Nicias, who seems to have been rather indecisive and who was certainly no astronomer. The army met with reverse after reverse, and at last it became clear that the only thing to do was to withdraw as quickly as possible. There should have been no difficulty about this, since Athens had always been a sea-power, but unfortunately Nicias delayed. He knew that an eclipse of the Moon was due, and he interpreted this as divine advice to stay where he was. By the time he ordered embarkation, his chance was gone. The Spartans attacked, and the Athenian force was so utterly defeated that very few of its members survived to return home. Most historians consider that the Sicilian disaster was the turning-point of the war. Within ten years Athens had been forced to surrender; Sparta was no substitute as a leader of the Greek city-states, and from that moment onward the fortunes of true Greece went downhill.

It was an extraordinary episode. At least fifty years earlier Anaxagoras had explained the cause of lunar eclipses quite clearly; he knew that they were due to the shadow of the Earth falling on to the Moon and temporarily cutting off the supply of direct sunlight. An educated man such as Nicias should have known that there was nothing mysterious about them. Had he been well-informed

The total eclipse at Aquilar in Spain in July 1860, from *The Illustrated London News*

about astronomy he would have ordered his ships to sail in time; the Athenian force would have been saved, and the whole story of the war would have been different. It is not too much to say that this one eclipse changed the course of European history.

During the following centuries the progress of science was steady, if not rapid. Men such as Plato wrote down their thoughts for the benefit of mankind; and then we come to Aristotle, who was not primarily an astronomer, but whose influence on human thought in general was to last for a very long time indeed.

Aristotle had no faith in the old theory of a flat Earth, and he described observations which, in his

Aristotle's view of the universe, showing the earth at its centre—but Aristotle's earth is a sphere. This picture was published in 1523

view, proved that the true shape must be that of a globe. This spherical form would be "the shape that a body naturally assumes when all parts of it tend toward the centre"—which seems to give some idea of the theory of gravitation. Aristotle then pointed out that one's view of the sky depends very largely upon where one happens to be; thus the brilliant southern star Canopus can be seen from Egypt, but not from Greece. Thirdly,

Aristotle referred to lunar eclipses. The shadow cast by the Earth on to the Moon has a curved edge, so that presumably the Earth's surface must also be curved.

All this was sound reasoning, but Aristotle could not bring himself to believe that the Earth could lie anywhere but at the centre of the universe. Also, he considered that the sky must be essentially unchanging. Therefore he was running no risk of being accused of heresy—but the charge could well have been levelled at his successor, Aristarchus of Samos, who was born about 310 BC, less than twenty years after Aristotle had died.

Aristarchus was a scientific revolutionary. He made a serious attempt to measure distances from the Moon and the Sun; and though his value for the Earth-Sun distance was much too small (five million miles, as against the real figure of 93 million miles) it was a great improvement on any previous estimate. He knew that although the Moon is smaller than the Earth, the Sun is larger; and—most important of all—he dethroned the Earth from its proud position in the centre of the universe, and put the Sun there instead.

Anaxagoras, long before, had been persecuted for holding views which were much less extreme than this, but there is no record that Aristarchus was threatened in any way. Instead, he was more or less ignored, and the philosophers who came after him went back to the idea of a central Earth. One reason for this was that Aristotle had laid down such a pattern—and who could dare to question Aristotle?

Then, somewhat later, Eratosthenes of Cyrene made a very accurate measurement of the size of the Earth. He was in charge of a great library at Alexandria, the town which had more or less replaced Athens as the cultural headquarters of Mediterranean learning. Eratosthenes learned that at noon on midsummer day the Sun was exactly overhead as seen from the city of Syene (the modern Assouan) some way up the Nile; but at this moment it was $7\frac{1}{2}$ degrees away from the overhead point as seen from Alexandria. A full circle contains 360 degrees, and $7\frac{1}{2}$ is about 1/50 of 360, so that if the Earth is spherical its circumference must be 50 times the distance between Alexandria and Syene.

Eratosthenes duly made the required measurements; according to legend (which may or may not be true), he estimated the distance from Alexandria to Syene by driving there in his coach and counting the number of turns made by the wheel. In any case, his final result was almost incredibly precise. It remained the best for over a thousand years, and was much nearer the truth than the value assumed by Christopher Columbus when he set out on his voyage to the New World in AD 1492—which goes some way toward explaining why Columbus eventually came home without having more than a vague idea of where he had been.

Aristarchus and Eratosthenes had one thing at least in common: they were observers, who made their calculations on the basis of what they themselves had seen. Moreover, they made no secret of their discoveries or their theories. Their attitude was very different from that of the old Egyptian priests, who were only too anxious to keep their knowledge to themselves.

There were no hints of scientific persecution during the late period of what we generally call the Greek period (though Ptolemy, whose work marked the grand climax, may have been Egyptian by birth). Certainly the last two major astronomers of the era, Hipparchus around 150 BC and Ptolemy two centuries later, were strictly scientific in their outlook. Both were brilliant men;

Part of Ptolemy's catalogue of stars, from the *Almagest*

## Longitudo et Latitudo ac Magnitudo stellarum fixarum

| Forme et Stelle | Lõgitudo | | | Pars | Lati^do | | Magni. |
|---|---|---|---|---|---|---|---|
| Stellatio Urse Minoris — Imago Prima | s | g | m | | g | m | |
| Illa que est super extremitatem caude | 2 | 0 | 10 | S | 66 | 0 | 3 |
| Illa que est post istam super caudam | 2 | 2 | 30 | S | 70 | 0 | 4 |
| Illa que est post eam in origine caude | 2 | 16 | 0 | S | 74 | 0 | 4 |
| Meridiana a latere antecedente laterum clunium | 2 | 29 | 40 | S | 75 | 40 | 4 |
| Septentrionalis ab hoc latere | 3 | 3 | 40 | S | 77 | 40 | 4 |
| Meridiana duarum que sunt in latere sequente | 3 | 17 | 10 | S | 72 | 50 | 2 |
| Septentrionalis ab hoc loco | 3 | 26 | 10 | S | 74 | 50 | 2 |
| He ergo sunt septem stelle. quarum in magnitudine secūda sunt due in tertia vna. ꝛ in qrta qttuoꝛ. | | | | | | | |
| Que est inter eas: ꝛ non est in forma. | | | | | | | |
| Maridiana duaꝝ q̃ st sup rectitudinē duaꝝ stellaꝝ q̃ sūt i latē sequēte | 3 | 13 | 0 | S | 71 | 10 | 4 |
| Stellatio Urse Maioris — Imago Secunda | | | | | | | |
| Illa que est super extremitatem muscide. | 2 | 25 | 20 | S | 39 | 50 | 4 |
| Antecedens duarum que sunt in duobus oculis. | 2 | 25 | 50 | S | 43 | 0 | 5 |
| Sequens earum | 2 | 26 | 20 | S | 43 | 0 | 5 |
| Antecedens duarum que sunt in fronte | 2 | 26 | 10 | S | 47 | 10 | 5 |
| Sequens earum | 2 | 27 | 40 | S | 47 | 0 | 5 |
| Illa que est super extremitatem auris antecedentis | 2 | 28 | 10 | S | 50 | 30 | 5 |
| Antecedens duarum que sunt in collo | 3 | 2 | 30 | S | 43 | 50 | 4 |
| Sequens earum | 3 | 9 | 30 | S | 44 | 20 | 4 |
| Declivior duarum earum que sunt in pectore ad septentrionem | 2 | 11 | 0 | S | 42 | 0 | 4 |
| Declivior earum ad meridiem | 2 | 10 | 0 | S | 44 | 0 | 4 .e.l. |
| Illa que est super genu sinistrum | 3 | 5 | 40 | S | 35 | 0 | 3 |
| Septētrionalis duaꝝ stellarū q̃ sūt ī extremitate pedis sinistri p̄cedēti | 3 | 6 | 30 | S | 29 | 20 | 3 |
| Meridiana earum | 3 | 5 | 20 | S | 28 | 30 | 3 |
| Illa que est super genu dextrum | 3 | 5 | 40 | S | 36 | 0 | 4 |
| Illa que est sub genu dextro | 3 | 17 | 50 | S | 33 | 3 | 4 |
| Illa que est super dorsum earum que sunt habentis quattuoꝛ latera | 3 | 22 | 40 | S | 49 | 0 | 2 |
| Illa que est super mirach eius | 3 | 2 | 10 | S | 44 | 30 | 2 |
| Illa que est super originem caude eius | 4 | 3 | 10 | S | 51 | 0 | 3 |
| Sequens earum: ꝛ est illa q̃ est super ancham sinistram posterioꝛem | 4 | 4 | 0 | S | 46 | 30 | 2 |
| Antecedens duarum que sunt in pede sinistro posterioꝛe | 3 | 22 | 40 | S | 29 | 30 | 3 |
| Sequens hanc | 3 | 24 | 10 | S | 28 | 15 | 3 |
| Illa que est in ventre genu sinistri | 4 | 1 | 40 | S | 35 | 15 | 4 |
| Septentrionalis duarū que sunt in pede dextro posterioꝛe | 4 | 9 | 50 | S | 25 | 50 | 3 |
| Declivior earum ad meridiem | 4 | 10 | 20 | S | 25 | 0 | 3 |
| Prima trium que sunt super caudam: ꝛ est altioꝛe | 4 | 12 | 10 | S | 53 | 30 | 2 |
| Media earum | 4 | 18 | 0 | S | 55 | 40 | 2 |
| Tertia: ꝛ est ea que est super extremitatem caude | 4 | 29 | 50 | S | 54 | 0 | 2 |
| Illarum ergo vigintiseptem stellarum in magnitudine secunda sunt sex. in tertia octo. in quarta octo. in quinta quinq;. | | | | | | | |
| Ille que sunt sub eis ꝛ non sunt in forma | | | | | | | |
| Stella elongata a cauda versus meridiem | 4 | 27 | 50 | S | 39 | 45 | 3 |
| Antecedens hanc: ꝛ est occultioꝛ ea | 4 | 20 | 10 | S | 41 | 20 | 5 |
| Declivioꝛ duarum que sunt in eo qđ est inter duos pedes antecedentes vrse ꝛ inter caput leonis ad meridiem. | 3 | 15 | 0 | S | 17 | 35 | 4 |
| Illa que est declivioꝛ ab hac ad septentrionem | 3 | 13 | 20 | S | 19 | 10 | 4 |
| Sequens stellarum trium reliquarum occultarum | 3 | 16 | 10 | S | 20 | 0 | oc. |
| Antecedens hanc | 3 | 12 | 10 | S | 22 | 45 | oc. |
| Illa que plus antecedit hanc | 3 | 11 | 10 | S | 23 | 15 | oc. |
| Illa que est inter duos pedes vrse antecedentes ꝛ geminos | 4 | 0 | 0 | S | 22 | 15 | oc. |
| Illarum ergo octo stellarum que non sunt in forma: in magnitudine tertia est vna. in quarta due. in quinta vna. ꝛ occulte quattuoꝛ. | | | | | | | |
| Stellatio Draconis — Imago Tertia | | | | | | | |
| Que est super linguam | 6 | 26 | 40 | S | 76 | 30 | 4 |
| Que est in oꝛe | 7 | 11 | 50 | S | 78 | 30 | 4 |

Hipparchus, in addition to drawing up a really good star-catalogue, discovered precession and also invented trigonometry. Ptolemy, still often called "the Prince of Astronomers", wrote a book which remains our main source of knowledge of ancient science. It has come down to us by way of its Arab translation; we call it the *Almagest.*

From a purely practical point of view, Ptolemy's achievements in geography may have been more important than his astronomy, because he drew up the first map of the known world which was based on measurement rather than guesswork and estimation. Obviously the method had to be astronomical, and Ptolemy used it well; even though his chart of the British Isles is distorted, with Scotland more or less back to front, it is quite recognizable. There was nothing the matter with his methods, and they marked the beginning of proper map-making—which would have been impossible without astronomical knowledge.

Ptolemy did not agree that the Sun could be the centre of the universe, and, like most of his predecessors, he regarded the Earth as supreme, but it seems likely that his reasons were scientific rather than religious. For instance, he believed that the world could not be spinning round, because the result would be a constant, very strong wind which would blow down everything in its path! We can see the fault in this reasoning clearly enough; but Ptolemy could not—and could hardly have been expected to do so.

On the other hand, he knew quite well that the Sun, Moon and planets could not move round the Earth at regular speeds in perfectly circular paths, as had been originally thought. He was an excellent observer, and his measurements of the positions of the planets as they moved against the stars showed that the whole problem was a very complicated one. Finally he adopted a system according to

A page from Ptolemy's *Almagest,* published in Venice in 1515 *(opposite)*

tis possibile est esse fm duos modos primos absolutos. Qꝛ si motus stellarum qui videtur esset in orbe cuius centrum estimatur esse centrum mundi: qd̓ est in superficie orbis signorum: ⁊ neqȝ esset aspectus oculorum nostrorum nisi a centro: non videretur in motu earum diuersitas. Quapropter estimamus ꝙ motus earū sint fm vnum duorum modorum. Aut supra orbes quorum centra non sunt centrū mundi: sed sunt egredientia ab ipso: ⁊ sunt motus eaꝝ medij. Aut sunt super orbes: quoꝝ centra sunt centrum mundi: sed non sunt supra ipsos fm sermonem absolute: sed sunt supra orbes alios: qui sunt supra hos orbes reuoluētes eas qui nominātur orbes reuoluentes stellas. ¶ Declarabitᷣ nāqȝ ꝙ possibile est: vt videantur fm vnumquemqȝ horum duorum modorum in temporibus equalibus trāsire super arcus diuersos orbis signorum: cuius centrum est centrum mundi. Describam autē cuiusqȝ horum duorum modorū exēplum: ⁊ primum ponam circulum orbis ecentrici.

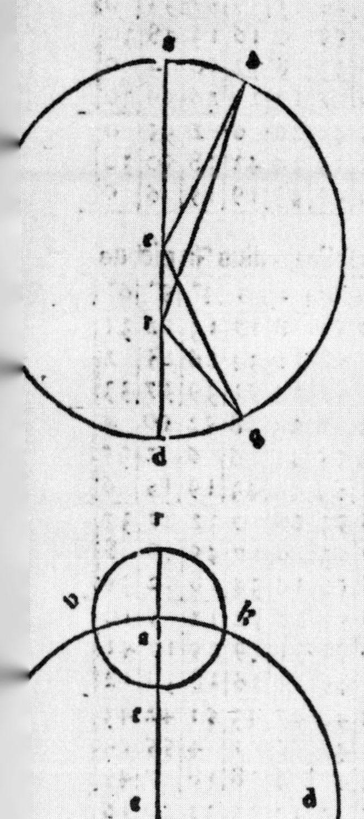

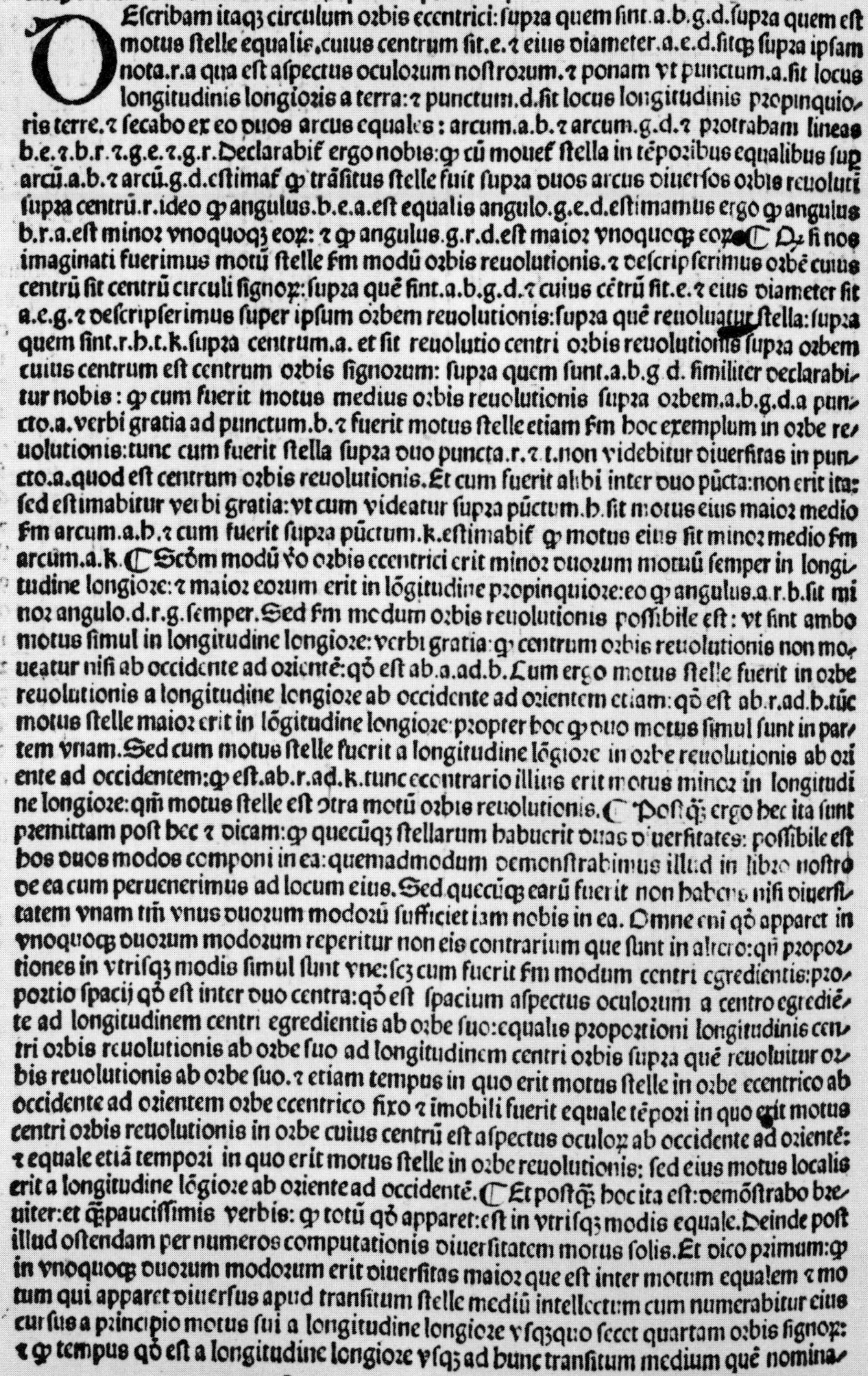

Describam itaqȝ circulum orbis ecentrici: supra quem sint. a. b. g. d. supra quem est motus stelle equalis. cuius centrum sit. e. ⁊ eius diameter. a. e. d. sitqȝ supra ipsam nota. r. a qua est aspectus oculorum nostrorum. ⁊ ponam vt punctum. a. sit locus longitudinis longioris a terra: ⁊ punctum. d. sit locus longitudinis propinquioris terre. ⁊ secabo ex eo duos arcus equales: arcum. a. b. ⁊ arcum. g. d. ⁊ protrabam lineas b. e. ⁊. b. r. ⁊. g. e. ⁊. g. r. Declarabitᷣ ergo nobis: ꝙ cū mouetᷣ stella in tēporibus equalibus sup arcū. a. b. ⁊ arcū. g. d. estimatᷣ ꝙ trāsitus stelle fuit supra duos arcus diuersos orbis reuoluti supra centrū. r. ideo ꝙ angulus. b. e. a. est equalis angulo. g. e. d. estimamus ergo ꝙ angulus b. r. a. est minor vnoquoqȝ eoꝝ: ⁊ ꝙ angulus. g. r. d. est maior vnoquoqȝ eoꝝ. ¶ Qꝛ si nos imaginati fuerimus motū stelle fm modū orbis reuolutionis. ⁊ descripserimus orbē cuius centrū sit centrū circuli signoꝝ: supra quē sint. a. b. g. d. ⁊ cuius cētrū sit. e. ⁊ eius diameter sit a. e. g. ⁊ descripserimus super ipsum orbem reuolutionis: supra quē reuoluatur stella: supra quem sint. r. h. t. k. supra centrum. a. et sit reuolutio centri orbis reuolutionis supra orbem cuius centrum est centrum orbis signorum: supra quem sunt. a. b. g. d. similiter declarabitur nobis: ꝙ cum fuerit motus medius orbis reuolutionis supra orbem. a. b. g. d. a puncto. a. verbi gratia ad punctum. b. ⁊ fuerit motus stelle etiam fm hoc exemplum in orbe reuolutionis: tunc cum fuerit stella supra duo puncta. r. ⁊. t. non videbitur diuersitas in puncto. a. quod est centrum orbis reuolutionis. Et cum fuerit alibi inter duo pūcta: non erit ita: sed estimabitur verbi gratia: vt cum videatur supra pūctum. h. sit motus eius maior medio fm arcum. a. h. ⁊ cum fuerit supra pūctum. k. estimabitᷣ ꝙ motus eius sit minor medio fm arcum. a. k. ¶ Scdm̄ modū vᵒ orbis ecentrici erit minor duorum motuū semper in longitudine longiore: ⁊ maior eorum erit in lōgitudine propinquiore: eo ꝙ angulus. a. r. b. sit minor angulo. d. r. g. semper. Sed fm modum orbis reuolutionis possibile est: vt sint ambo motus simul in longitudine longiore: verbi gratia: ꝙ centrum orbis reuolutionis non moueatur nisi ab occidente ad orientē: qd̓ est ab. a. ad. b. Cum ergo motus stelle fuerit in orbe reuolutionis a longitudine longiore ab occidente ad orientem etiam: qd̓ est ab. r. ad. h. tūc motus stelle maior erit in lōgitudine longiore: propter hoc ꝙ duo motus simul sunt in partem vnam. Sed cum motus stelle fuerit a longitudine lōgiore in orbe reuolutionis ab oriente ad occidentem: ꝙ est. ab. r. ad. k. tunc econtrario illius erit motus minor in longitudine longiore: qm̄ motus stelle est ꝯtra motū orbis reuolutionis. ¶ Postq̄ȝ ergo hec ita sunt premittam post hec ⁊ dicam: ꝙ quecūqȝ stellarum habuerit duas diuersitates: possibile est hos duos modos componi in ea: quemadmodum demonstrabimus illud in libro nostro de ea cum peruenerimus ad locum eius. Sed quecūqȝ earū fuerit non habens nisi diuersitatem vnam tm̄ vnus duorum modorū sufficiet iam nobis in ea. Omne eni qd̓ apparet in vnoquoqȝ duorum modorum reperitur non eis contrarium que sunt in altero: qm̄ proportiones in vtrisqȝ modis simul sunt vne: scȝ cum fuerit fm modum centri egredientis: proportio spacij qd̓ est inter duo centra: qd̓ est spacium aspectus oculorum a centro egrediēte ad longitudinem centri egredientis ab orbe suo: equalis proportioni longitudinis centri orbis reuolutionis ab orbe suo ad longitudinem centri orbis supra quē reuoluitur orbis reuolutionis ab orbe suo. ⁊ etiam tempus in quo erit motus stelle in orbe ecentrico ab occidente ad orientem orbe ecentrico fixo ⁊ imobili fuerit equale tēpori in quo erit motus centri orbis reuolutionis in orbe cuius centrū est aspectus oculoꝝ ab occidente ad orientē: ⁊ equale etiā tempori in quo erit motus stelle in orbe reuolutionis: sed eius motus localis erit a longitudine lōgiore ab oriente ad occidentē. ¶ Et postq̄ȝ hoc ita est: demōstrabo breuiter: et q̄ȝ paucissimis verbis: ꝙ totū qd̓ apparet: est in vtrisqȝ modis equale. Deinde post illud ostendam per numeros computationis diuersitatem motus solis. Et dico primum: ꝙ in vnoquoqȝ duorum modorum erit diuersitas maior que est inter motum equalem ⁊ motum qui apparet diuersus apud transitum stelle mediū intellectum cum numerabitur eius cursus a principio motus sui a longitudine longiore vsqȝ quo secet quartam orbis signoꝝ: ⁊ ꝙ tempus qd̓ est a longitudine longiore vsqȝ ad hunc transitum medium quē nomina-

which the various celestial bodies moved round the Earth in what now seems an artificial manner. A planet revolved round a "deferent"—an imaginary point which itself travelled round the world in a perfect circle. As more and more errors came to light, Ptolemy had to introduce more and more complications, until at last the whole system was hopelessly cumbersome; but—and this is the vital fact—it did agree with the observations.

The system is always called the Ptolemaic. Ptolemy did not invent it, but he brought it to its highest degree of perfection, and it was accepted by almost everybody for more than a thousand years after his death.

Over the long period between the lives of Thales and Ptolemy (which, incidentally, is as long as the time which has elapsed since the Crusades!) we can detect a change in outlook. Pure observation has given way to a conscious effort to understand and interpret the universe. Moreover, we can see that the astronomy of ancient times was very much a practical study. Then, as now, it was the basis of all timekeeping, map-making and navigation. It would be overstating the case to claim that astronomy affected the lives of the mass of the people, but the farmers and the traders, particularly, would have been in a sad plight without it.

Above all, man had started to realize that he could not be quite so important as he had once thought. Perhaps the attitude can best be summed up in the words of Ptolemy himself:

"I know that I am mortal and the creature of a day; but when I search out the massed wheeling circles of the stars, my feet no longer touch the earth."

## CHAPTER FOUR

# *Man the Astrologer*

Only a few days ago I had a letter from a man who had been watching the BBC television programme *The Sky at Night*, which I have presented monthly since 1957. He had a problem, and wanted to consult me. He had the chance to buy a partnership in a business firm; would I please consult the stars, cast his horoscope, and tell him whether this would be a good time to take such an important step?

Alas, I was of no help to him, and could only reply soothingly, explaining that astronomy and astrology are very definitely not the same thing. This is by no means the only letter I have had along similar lines, and even today it is an undeniable fact that astrology retains a strong following. In some Eastern countries, notably India, it is still considered really important—and only recently Mrs Gandhi, Prime Minister of India, went so far as to alter the date of a general election on the basis of astrological advice. True, she won a sweeping victory at the polls; but one may well doubt whether the stars had anything to do with it!

All this may seem a great leap in time from a discussion of Ptolemy's *Almagest*, but it is probably best to deal with the whole subject of astrology without further delay, because for many centuries it was ranked as the equal of scientific astronomy. Indeed, the two were classed as indistinguishable, and among believers in astrology we must include not only Hipparchus and Ptolemy but also the Arabs, Johannes Kepler, and Sir Isaac Newton himself. Therefore, astrology forms a link between the ancient world and the modern age.

As with astronomy, we can have no clear idea of when it began. Undoubtedly it had its origins in the days when men looked up at the sky and believed it to have been created for Man's special benefit. One of the famous Greek philosophers, Eudoxus, identified various celestial bodies with the mythological gods, and the first true astrological textbook which has come down to us dates from the third century BC. Its aim, of course, was to provide a method of forecasting the future—an ambition which has persisted all through subsequent history, from the Greeks right down to the modern astrologer who sits on the end of a seaside pier examining his crystal ball. There is, however, an important distinction between the old astrology

The Planets in Relation to Earth

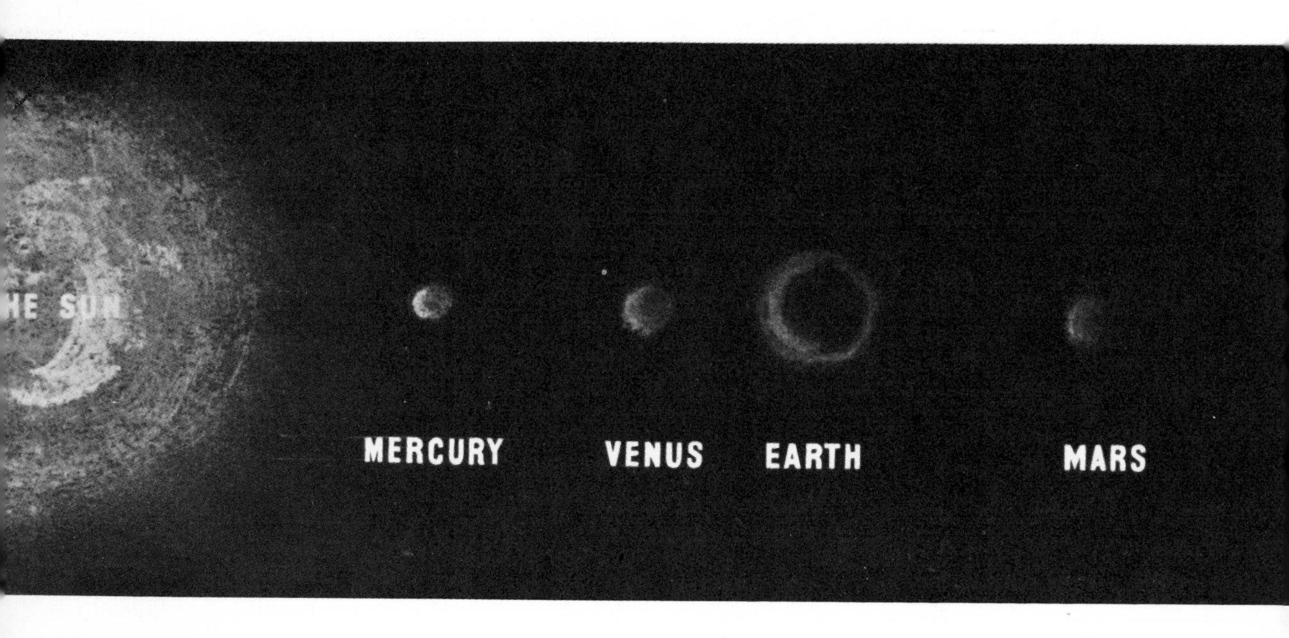

A 17th-Century astrologer casts a horoscope

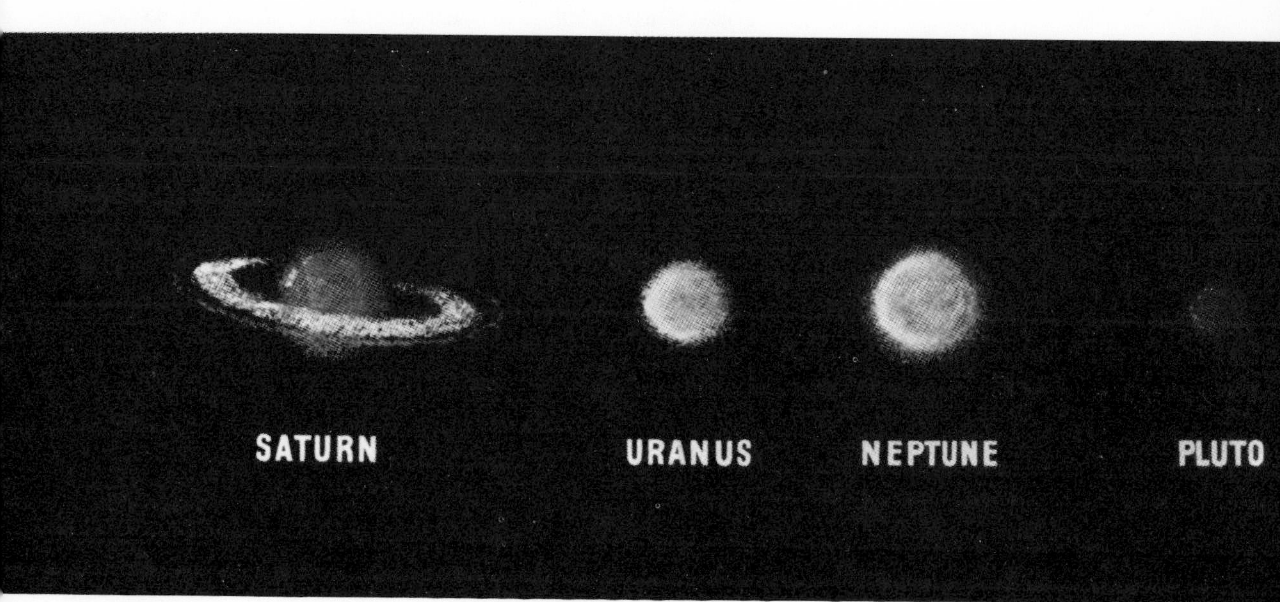

and the new. Modern astrology affects the lives only of the ignorant or the gullible. Ancient astrology more or less controlled the destinies of vast numbers of people. The Chinese writer Wang Ch'ung, about AD 50, said that "Heaven's power to bestow grace or disgrace upon human beings is distributed among the stars," and the professional astrologer was a very important person indeed.

The view was not universal. In Rome, men such as Cicero had no patience with astrology, and now and then there were official campaigns against astrologers who were becoming powerful enough to constitute a real threat to Emperors or governments. In AD 570 Isidorus, Bishop of Seville, even wrote a book in which he made a clear distinction between astronomy and astrology. But in general the astrologers were regarded as extremely valuable, and to question their teachings was both dangerous and unwise.

Astrology is based on the apparent positions of the Sun, Moon and planets as seen against the stars. For instance, if (say) the planet Mars appears in the pattern of stars making up the constellation of Taurus, the Bull, then Mars is said to be "in" Taurus. Of course this is meaningless; Mars, a planet in our own Solar System, is comparatively close to us, whereas the stars are immensely remote. The situation may be compared with that of a sparrow seen flying at a height of a few feet, against a background of high cloud. It would hardly be reasonable to claim that the sparrow is then "in" the cloud.

Moreover, the stars are not equally distant from us, and the stars in any particular constellation are not genuinely connected with each other. This was something which the ancient astronomers could not realize. Because the stars appeared relatively fixed, it was believed that they must be fastened on to a solid sphere—and that it was this invisible

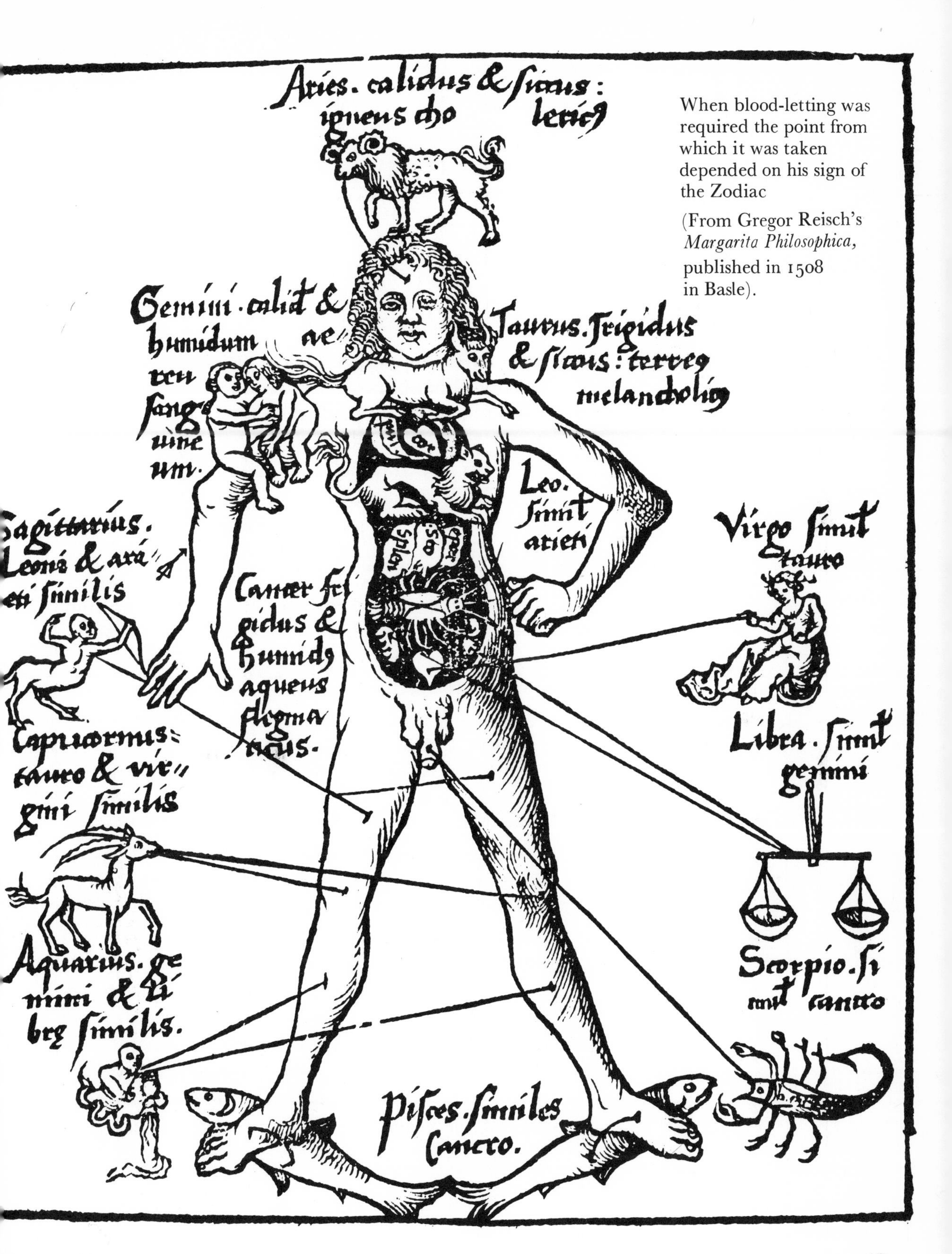


When blood-letting was required the point from which it was taken depended on his sign of the Zodiac

(From Gregor Reisch's *Margarita Philosophica*, published in 1508 in Basle).

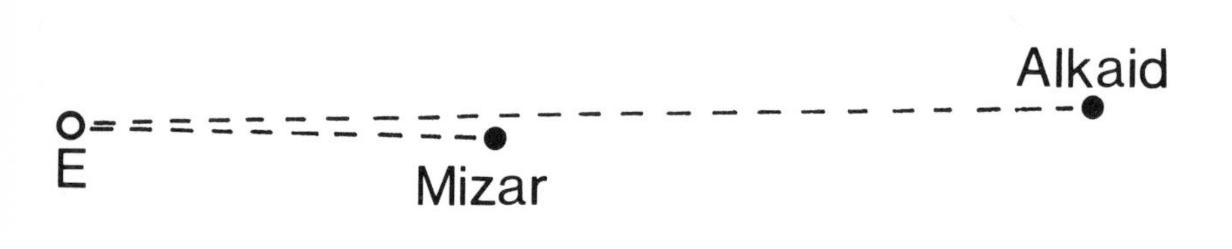


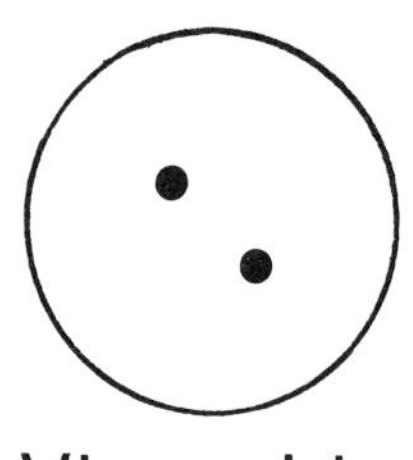


Star Alignment. Alkaid is much more remote than Mizar, but from Earth they seem fairly close together in the sky

sphere which revolved round the Earth once in twenty-four hours. It would follow that the stars would all be at the same distance. In fact, nothing could be more wide of the mark. Consider, for example, the stars in the famous constellation of Ursa Major (the Great Bear), which most people can recognize; it is often nicknamed the Plough. Of the two stars in the Bear's tail, Mizar is rather less than 500 million million miles away from us, whereas Alkaid is well over 1000 million million miles. In fact, Alkaid is considerably further from Mizar than we are; and the side-by-side appearance is due to nothing more than a line of sight effect. The diagram should make this clear.

There is also the question of the constellations themselves. The original division of the stars into separate groups was done in order to help in describing and identifying them, but the choice of constellations—and their names—was very open, because there are few well-marked patterns. The names were taken from Classical mythology, and it has been said that the sky is a vast story-book; among the list of forty-eight constellations given by Ptolemy we find Hercules, Pegasus the flying horse, and all the main characters in the legend of Perseus and the Gorgon's head, to say nothing of Orion the hunter, the "Heavenly Twins" Castor and Pollux, and the great ship which carried the Argonauts in their quest of the Golden Fleece. True, some of the names are less intriguing, and modern additions may be positively dull; there is nothing romantic about the Furnace, the Microscope or the Sculptor's Tools. But in any case, very few of the constellations bear any resemblance to the shape of the object commemorated. If you doubt me, try making a queen out of the stars in Cassiopeia.

Because the bodies of the Solar System move in very much the same plane, the planets keep to a well-defined belt in the sky known as the Zodiac. There are twelve Zodiacal constellations, of which the most prominent are the Ram, the Bull, the

Venus and the activities governed by it. This was considered a female planet, cold, moist and temperate

Twins, the Lion, the Virgin, the Scorpion and the Archer. Aries, the Ram, used to be the first constellation of the Zodiac, because the Sun passed through it at the start of spring in the northern hemisphere of the Earth; but the effects of precession, described in Chapter II, have altered things considerably. The spring equinox

Astrologers casting a horoscope for a child at the moment of its birth

Mars was considered a male, fiery and hot planet, and those born under Mars were unruly, lawless and loved violence

now lies in the next-door group of Pisces, the Fishes, which contains no bright stars. Aries should really be counted as twelfth in the Zodiacal list instead of first, and the astrological signs are out of step with the constellations,

A horoscope is usually cast for the moment of a child's birth. Anyone born on, say, 4th March will be a "Piscean," because on that day the Sun is in the sign of Pisces. Astrologers will claim that this child's character and destiny will be markedly different from that of another child born on April 4, for instance, because the April baby will be an "Arian." The apparent positions of the Moon and planets are also taken into account, and the resulting horoscope looks highly complicated and impressive—though actually it has no meaning or significance whatsoever.

There is no real point in giving further details about astrology itself, and it is quite true to say that sincere astrologers (of whom there are many) make no attempt to explain just *how* they believe the planets affect a person's character. All they can do is to claim that "astrology works." Unfortunately, it is quite easy to show that the percentage of correct predictions is just what would be expected by sheer chance. Sometimes the forecasts are right—but, as a famous judge once said, "It is impossible always to be wrong."

In early times, and even in the period graced by Hipparchus and Ptolemy, there was every excuse for belief in astrology. If the stars formed a backcloth, and the planets existed solely for Man's benefit, they might be expected to act as signs. No wonder, then, that astrologers were classed as men of great power and learning. Yet it is also clear that belief in astrology also means belief in the supreme importance of Earth and its inhabitants, and this may well have been one of the reasons why most of the Greeks, far-sighted though they were, discarded the idea that our world might be in motion round the Sun.

During the period of Roman greatness, astrology had a rather chequered career. It is certainly true that in AD 45, that extraordinary man Claudius, the Emperor who really conquered Britain, made a public announcement to the effect that an eclipse which happened to fall on his birthday was merely a natural phenomenon, and did not foretell any disaster. But after the so-called Dark Ages which followed the fall of Rome, astrology became

The Moon was female, moist, and cold. This illustration shows the activities it governed

Luna.

all-important. Science was revived mainly by the Arabs, who were astrologers first and astronomers second.

To the Arabs, astronomical observation was needed in various ways. It was always essential to know the direction of the holy city of Mecca, and this was best done by checking the positions of the stars. For this sort of study Ptolemy's great scientific book was used, and fortunately it was translated into Arabic. This is the only reason why it has come down to us. The magnificent library at

The Earth, the seasonal occupation, and the signs of the Zodiac, from a translation of the *Shepheards Kalendar* into English at the beginning of the 16th Century

Alexandria, once controlled by Eratosthenes, was destroyed, a fact which scholars have never ceased to regret. There is a story that the destruction was deliberate, and was carried out at the orders of an Arab ruler, on the grounds that if the books agreed with the Koran they were superfluous, whereas if they disagreed with the Koran they were heretical. This is probably untrue, but at any rate the books were permanently lost.

For horoscope-casting, the astrologers needed good catalogues of the positions of the stars in the sky. For a time they used Ptolemy's, but from about the 9th century AD the Arab observers began to draw up better ones. They also needed to know more about the movements of the planets, and this problem also they tackled with great success. In fact, their astrology meant that they made fundamental advances in astronomy itself. There was no distinction between an astrologer and an astronomer—and, needless to say, there was no suggestion that the Earth could be anything but the central body of the universe.

It was ironical, then, that the last great astronomer of the Arab school met his death mainly because of his belief in astrology. His name was Ulugh Beigh, grandson of the Oriental warrior Tamerlane. He set up an observatory at his capital (Samarkand), and produced the best star catalogue of the time, as well as establishing a full-scale Academy of Science. However, he cast the horoscope of his eldest son, and discovered that the boy was destined to kill him. Immediately he dismissed his son, and stripped him of all honours—with the result that the young man rebelled, attacked his father's capital, and had Ulugh Beigh murdered.

This was in the fifteenth century, by which time science had been re-born in Western Europe. There were even faint signs of disagreement with the idea of a central Earth. Now, however, there was a new force to be reckoned with: the Christian Church, which was violently opposed to any attempt to question Man's supreme importance. For the moment there was no real trouble, but the indications were there.

Meanwhile, astrology had reached its peak. The leaders of nations depended very largely on it, and everywhere its influence was felt. Of course the extent of this influence varied, and was certainly much less in Britain than in most other countries, but it was virtually unchallenged. Now and then astrological forecasts caused widespread panic. One of these was sparked off in 1524 by a famous German astrologer named Johann Stoeffler, who found (correctly) that in February of that year several planets would lie close together in the sky, in the constellation of Pisces, the Fishes. Stoeffler announced that the inevitable result would be a major flood. In the terror which followed dozens of people were killed; the President of Toulouse University spent weeks in building an ark, and the Elector of Brandenburg collected all his portable possessions and repaired to the top of a mountain, where he remained for some time. Needless to say there was no flood, but, significantly, Stoefflers's reputation remained high.

It must be admitted that observational astronomy benefited from the needs of astrologers, but theoretical astronomy was definitely held back. Astrologers had to regard the Earth as the central body, and this meant that it must also be exceptionally important in the universe. Official religion held the same view. But as science advanced, astrology retreated. True, some of the great figures of later years were sympathetic to it, but others were sceptical—notably the first Astronomer Royal, John Flamsteed, who took charge of the astronomical observatory at

Greenwich founded in 1675 by order of King Charles II. Flamsteed cast the Observatory's horoscope, but ended it with the words "Risum teneatis, amici?"—or, in English, "Can you help laughing, friends?" It hardly seems that Flamsteed took his astrology very seriously.

Those born under the Moon love geometry and related arts, and are phlegmatic in temperament

In those days, of course, very few people could read and write. The invention of printing made a great difference eventually, but so long as the "common people" had to depend upon what they were told by word of mouth it was not easy for them to think about matters beyond their everyday life. Therefore astrology, like astronomy, was more or less confined to the wealthy and the educated classes. With the advance of true knowledge, astrology was bound to decline—and it did. Whereas it had been surprisingly strong in Stoeffler's time, and even in Flamsteed's, it had begun to fall out of favour well before 1800, and by the end of the nineteenth century it had ceased to be regarded as a proper science.

The reason for this is not hard to point out. Man had been forced to realize that far from being supreme, he was utterly unimportant in the universe as a whole, and his entire outlook on life was affected. Yet the changeover was anything but painless, and there was much suffering before the battle against superstition and bigotry was finally won.

CHAPTER FIVE

# *Rebellious Thought!*

During the seventeenth century a famous Churchman, Archbishop Ussher of Armagh, made a firm announcement about the origin of the Earth. The world, he said, had been created at ten o'clock in the morning of 26th October, 4004 BC. Ussher's methods were not really scientific; what he did was to add up the ages of the Patriarchs in the Old Testament and make some equally irrelevant calculations. Yet the official Church authorities accepted his findings without question, and it was a long time before they could bring themselves to believe that the world could be much older than a few thousand years.

I mention Ussher here because his attitude was, in its way, so typical. He believed that Man had been specially created, and that the race of Earthmen is the most important thing in the entire universe. Clearly, then, it followed that the Earth itself must be supreme—just as Ptolemy had maintained so long before. There must be an all-powerful God watching over us, and the idea that other races might exist on other planets would have seemed, to Ussher, much too ridiculous to be considered for a moment.

And yet there was already a great deal of scientific evidence that such was not the case. The

> There is more religion in men's science, than there is science in their religion.
> HENRY DAVID THOREAU
>
> Every great scientific truth goes through three stages. First, people say it conflicts with the Bible. Next, they say it has been discovered before. Lastly, they say they have always believed it.
> BENNETT CERF
>
> There more things in heaven and earth, Horatio, than are dreamt of in your philosophy.
> *Hamlet,* SHAKESPEARE

suggestion that the Earth is an ordinary planet, moving round the Sun, had been backed up by a mass of convincing evidence. The battle between science and prejudice had been well and truly joined, and it lasted for well over a hundred years.

The first broadside was fired in the year 1543 by Copernicus, a Polish priest. It took the form of a book, the title of which can be translated into English as *Concerning the Revolutions of the Celestial Bodies.* Copernicus had studied mathematics, and had come to the conclusion that the accepted view of the universe—Earth in the middle, with the Sun, Moon, planets and stars moving round it—must be untrue. In his own words, "Why should we not be willing to acknowledge that the *appearance* of a daily rotation belongs to the heavens, its *actuality* to the Earth? The relation is similar to that of which Virgil's Aeneas says: 'We sail out of the harbour, and the countries and cities recede.'" It followed, of course, that the idea of a solid sky could be given up.

Copernicus spent many years over his calculations, and finally arrived at a theory quite different from Ptolemy's. The essential difference was that the Sun, not the Earth, held the central position. This was Copernicus' great contribution to science. Most of his other ideas were wrong—and in particular he was quite sure that all the paths of the bodies in the sky must be perfectly circular. The circle was the "perfect" form, and nothing short of perfection could be allowed in the heavens.

But though Copernicus had his book ready well before 1540, he did not publish it. He had an uneasy feeling that the Christian Church would object. To remove the Earth from the centre of the universe might easily be regarded as heretical, and in those days heretics were not treated with kid gloves. So Copernicus remained silent. He allowed his book to be issued only when he

Is it so bad then to be misunderstood? Pythagoras was misunderstood, and Socrates, and Jesus, and Luther, and Copernicus, and Galileo, and Newton, and every pure and wise spirit that ever took flesh. To be great is to be misunderstood.

EMERSON

Look at the stars! Look,
look up at the skies!
O look at all the fire-folk
sitting in the air!
The bright boroughs, the
circle-citadels there!

G. M. HOPKINS

himself was dying, and it is said that he lived only just long enough to see the first printed copies. Moreover, unknown to him, the publisher had added an introduction claiming that the ideas put forward in the book were mere theories, and were not meant to be taken literally.

Copernicus was right; the Church was hostile. The Catholic authorities made their attitude clear from the outset, and, for that matter, so did the reformers; one of the fiercest critics of the "Copernican theory" was Martin Luther, who asked "Who is this fool?" But the crisis was slow to develop, and the arguments raged only between men of power and learning. Neither were these arguments genuinely scientific, because from a purely observational point of view it was impossible to prove which of the two theories must be correct.

The next character in the story was a Dane, Tycho Brahe. In 1576 he set up an observatory at Hven, an island in the Baltic a few miles from Malmö, and began to work upon a new and more accurate star catalogue. Telescopes still lay in the future; but Tycho was a splendid observer, and his catalogue proved to be far better than anything which had been drawn up before. Also, Tycho made detailed measurements of the movements of the planets, particularly Mars. He left Hven in 1596, after a series of quarrels with the Danish court, and ended his days in Bohemia as Imperial Mathematician to the Holy Roman Emperor. His last assistant was a German, Johannes Kepler; and when Tycho died, in 1601, Kepler came into possession of all the observations.

Tycho was a colourful character. He was a firm believer in astrology, and he was quite sure that the Earth must be the centre of all things—though he was equally dissatisfied with Ptolemy's theory, and believed that the planets moved round the Sun,

The Universe is not hostile, nor yet is it friendly. It is simply indifferent.
JOHN HAYNES HOLMES

Reason hath moons, but moons not hers,
Lie mirror'd on her sea,
Confounding her astronomers,
But, O! delighting me.
RALPH HODGSON

EFFIGIES TYCHONIS BRAHE O.F.
ÆDIFICII ET INSTRUMENTORVM
ASTRONOMICORVM STRVCTORIS
Aº. DOMINI 1587 ÆTATIS SVÆ. 40

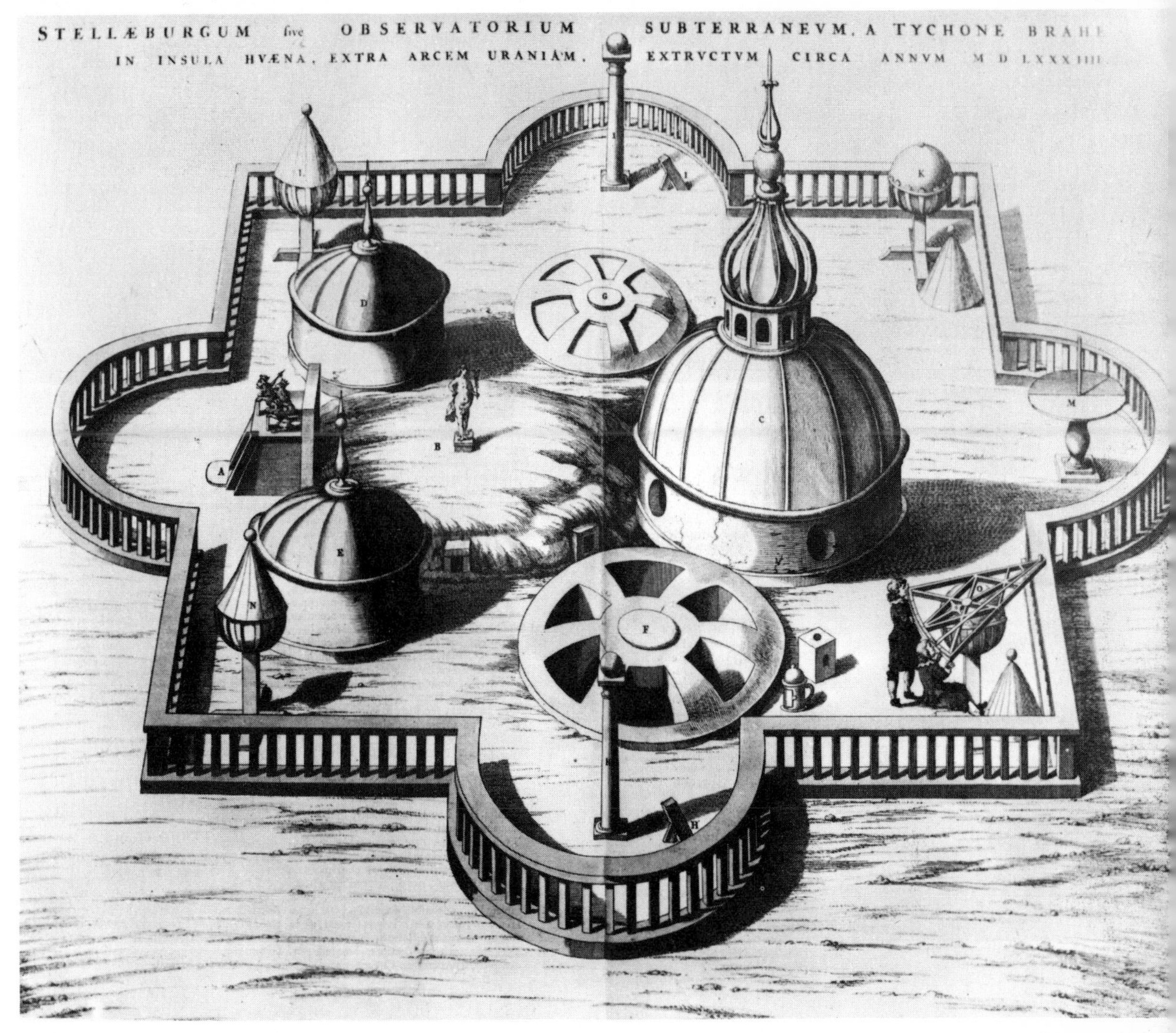


Tycho Brahe's Observatory on the Island of Hven

though the Sun itself followed a path round the Earth. He was hasty, intolerant and often cruel; his observatory included a prison (to hold tenants who would not pay him their rents) and in his retinue there was a pet dwarf. Yet Hven became very much of a scientific centre, and among the visitors there was the King of Scotland, afterwards James I of England. Nobody used the observatory or Tycho's castle after his departure, and today almost nothing of it remains.

Tycho Brahe's mural quadrant

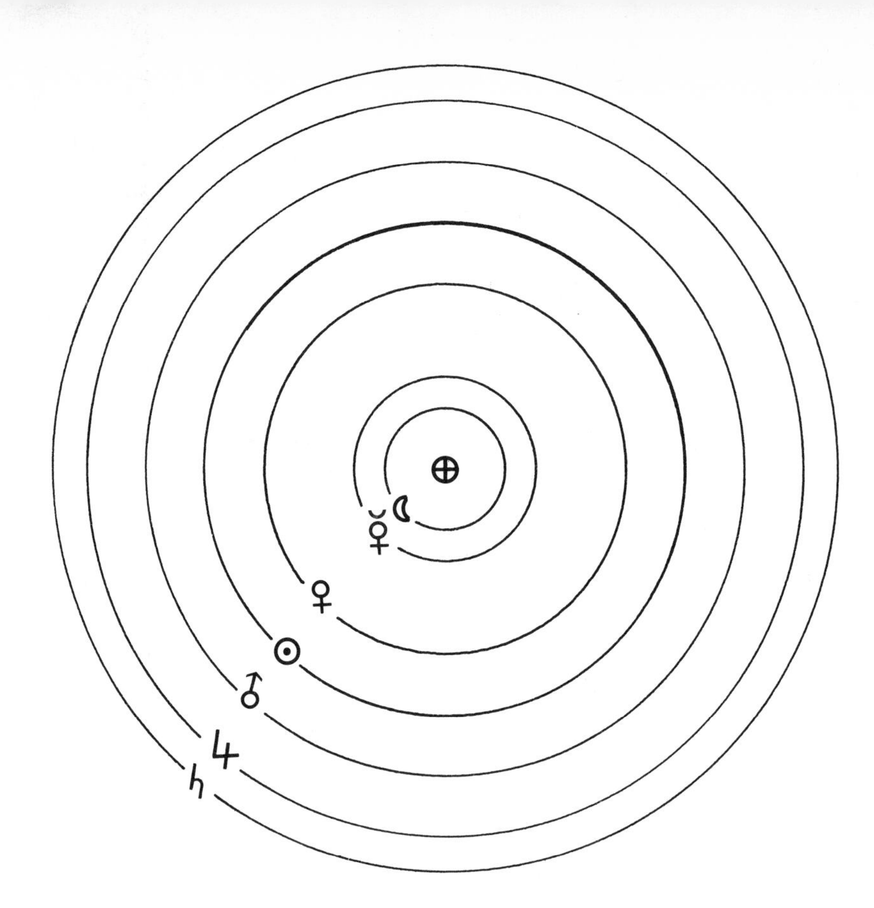


PTOLEMY

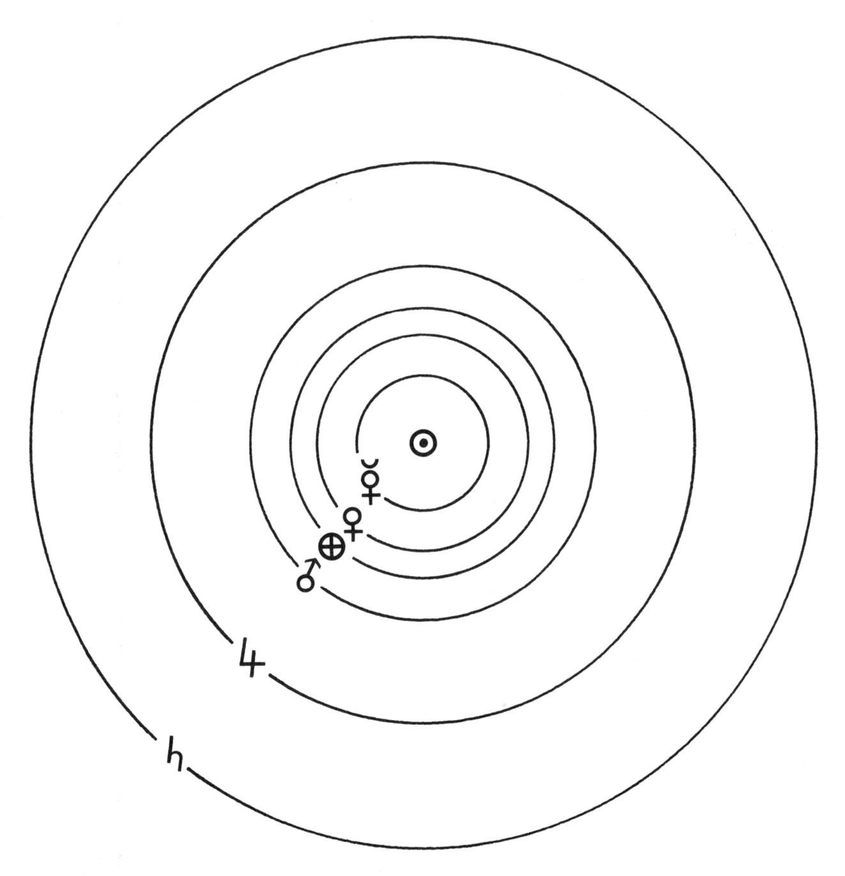




COPERNICUS

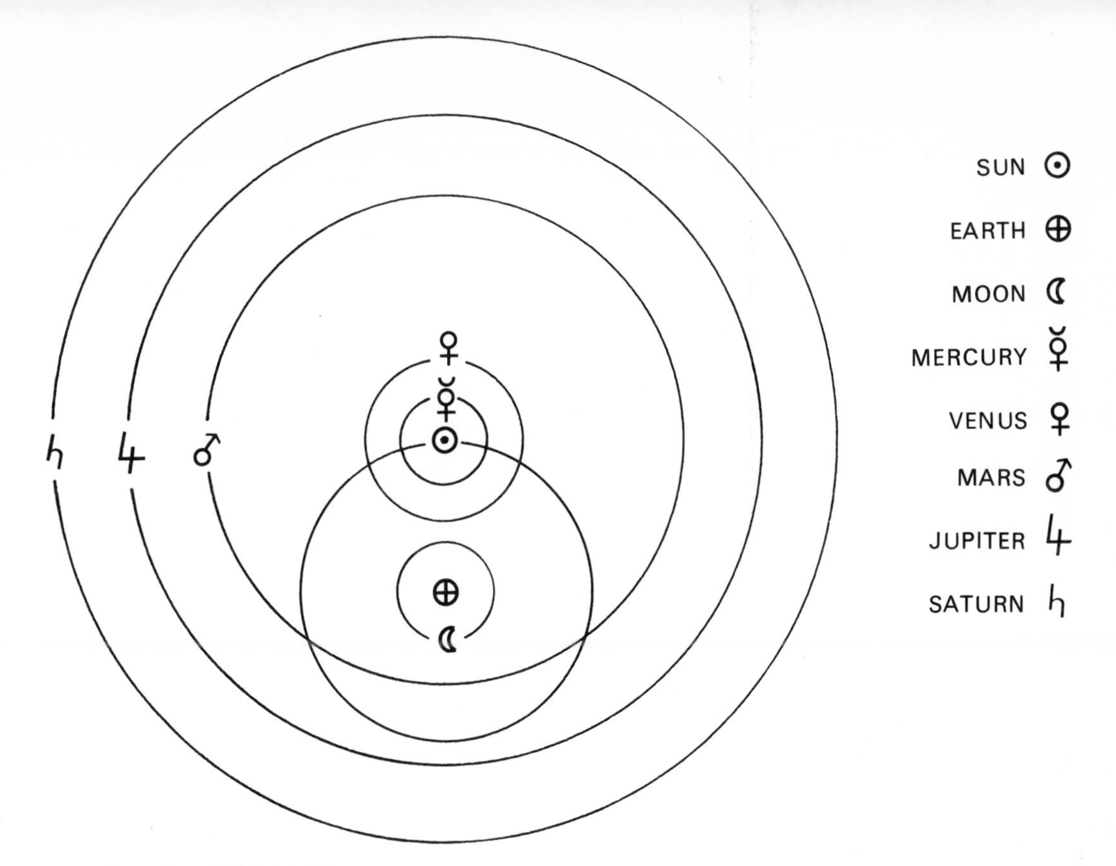


Early theories of the Universe (*above and opposite*)

## TYCHO BRAHE

There was one episode which affected the whole of Tycho's career. In 1572 a brilliant new star blazed out in the constellation of Cassiopeia, and became bright enough to be seen with the naked eye in broad daylight. We know it to have been a supernova—an immense explosion, in which a star destroyed itself and blew most of its material away into space. Tycho could not know this, but at least the remarkable star showed that Aristotle had been wrong in saying that the heavens were unchanging. As a good astrologer, Tycho predicted that the star foretold disasters of all kinds; but as an equally good astronomer he made careful observations of it, so that we know just how it behaved. It remained visible to the naked eye for several months, and radio waves from its remnant can still be detected today.

Meantime, the battle between the two theories of the universe had become fiercer. It reached a climax in 1600, when a philosopher named Giordano Bruno was burned at the stake in Rome. It is not true to say that Bruno's fate was due to his belief in a central Sun; he had committed many heresies in the eyes of the Church, but his defence of Copernicus certainly did not help him. Whatever evidence might be produced, the Church was determined to stamp out any ideas that the Earth might be an ordinary planet. Such heresy would strike at the very roots of Christian dogma.

Tycho, of course, was in no danger at all, because he never doubted the supreme importance of the Earth and its inhabitants; but some of his contemporaries thought differently. Johannes Kepler was in a strange position. He was no observer, but as a theorist he was Tycho's superior, and when he began to study the observations made at Hven he found that none of the current theories would fit the facts. The movements of Mars provided the essential clues, but for a long time Kepler could not find the key. Finally he did so, and produced the three Laws of Planetary Motion upon which all later work has been based. The one which conerns us here is the first: *A planet moves round the Sun in an elliptical orbit, with the Sun lying at one of the foci.* The Earth's orbit is very nearly a circle—but it is an ellipse, not a circle, and the difference is all-important. The insistence on "perfect circles" had to be given up.

Kepler had an unhappy life; at one period he had to fight a long battle to save his mother from being burned as a witch, and he was plagued by poverty and ill-health. However, he escaped violent persecution, and in a way he forms a bridge between the old science and the new; he cast horoscopes (though whether he took them seriously is doubtful) and he was very much of a mystic.

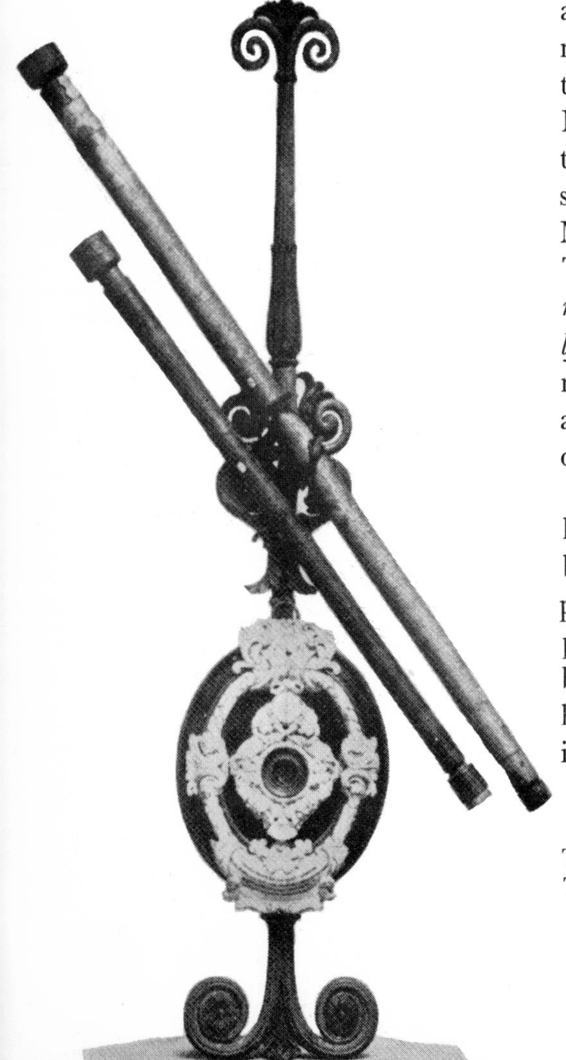

Two of Galileo's original telescopes, preserved in the Tribuna di Galileo, Florence

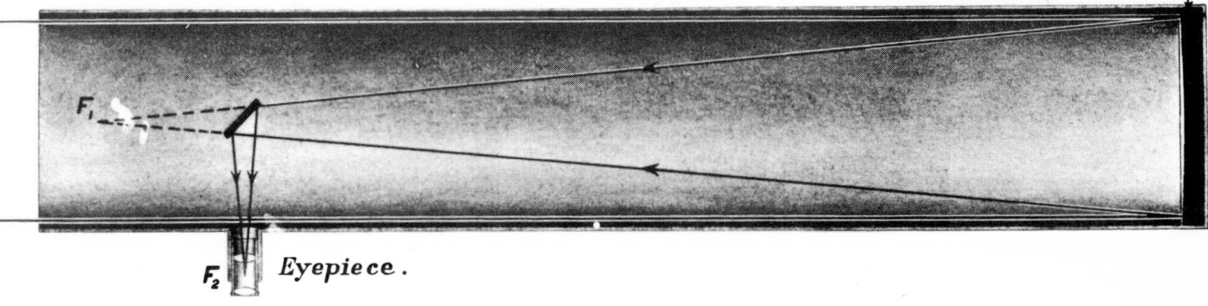


*Diagram illustrating*
NEWTONIAN TELESCOPE.

Kepler's first two Laws were published in 1609. In the same year Galileo Galilei, the great Italian scientist who really founded the science of experimental mechanics, made the first systematic observations with the help of the newly-invented telescope. With his primitive "optic tube" Galileo made a series of spectacular discoveries; he saw the mountains and craters of the Moon, the moons of Jupiter, the countless stars in the Milky Way, and much else. He had long since decided that the Copernican theory was correct, and his telescopic work made him even more certain. For instance, it had always been claimed that everything in the sky revolved round the Earth—but there could be no doubt that the four Jovian moons moved not round the Earth, but round Jupiter.

This is not the place to go into Galileo's scientific reasoning; we are concerned more with the social aspects of the argument. Galileo was tactless as well as outspoken, and he made the grave mistake of supposing that the Church authorities would listen to reason. Of course they did not, and there is a story that one leading cleric refused to look through Galileo's telescope on the grounds that it had been bewitched. Not long afterwards the cleric died, and Galileo is said to have commented that he ought to have had a splendid view of Jupiter's moons on his way to Heaven.

Eventually a priest named Lorini wrote to the Holy Office in Rome, condemning Galileo for trying "to defend an opinion which appears to be quite contrary to the sacred text" (that is to say, the Bible). At first Galileo was not worried;

Newton's Telescope

Telescopes used by
Galileo and Torricelli

the Pope, Urban VIII, was an old friend of his. Unfortunately Urban's attitude changed with dramatic suddenness. He felt that Galileo had made fun of him by caricaturing him as the simpleton in a book called *Dialogue on the Two Great World Systems*; and in 1633 Galileo was summoned to Rome, put on trial, and condemned for heresy. He was even made to "curse, abjure and detest" the false theory that the Earth moves round the Sun. He was then removed to his villa at Arcetri and cut off from the world; to add to his misery he lost his sight. When he died, the Pope refused to allow a monument to be erected over his tomb, because the dead man "had given rise to the greatest scandal throughout Christendom."

Science is organized knowledge.
HERBERT SPENCER

For Art and Science cannot exist but in minutely organized particulars.
BLAKE

Never has there been a clearer case of blind prejudice. It affected not only the principal characters in the story, but also the general outlook of educated people, simply because the schools and universities were forbidden to teach the Copernican theory—just as until recently it was illegal to teach the theory of evolution in the American State of Tennessee. There was no scientific excuse, because Kepler's work, to say nothing of Galileo's own observations with telescopes, had shown that the old ideas were obviously wrong. It is also worth noting that Galileo's book was placed on the Papal Index, so that to read it was a serious offence. The book was not finally removed from the Index until just before Queen Victoria came to the British throne!

We can see, then, that the Church was making a desperate effort to keep its hold upon the people. Scientific evidence was unimportant in the eyes of Christian authorities, and presumably they hoped that after a while the whole heretical episode would be forgotten. In fact, Galileo was the last great scientist to be persecuted, because as the years went by the evidence became so overwhelming that it could not be questioned. Before the end of the seventeenth century Sir Isaac Newton had published his work upon gravitation, and so put a final end to the long battle. By 1700 the Ptolemaic theory was not only dead, but buried.

All this had marked effects upon the general attitude toward science, and toward mankind itself. Suggestions of "life elsewhere" no longer seemed ridiculous—despite men such as Ussher at an even later stage—and if the Earth were an ordinary planet, there seemed no reason to doubt that the Sun must be an ordinary star. Human conceit had taken its first real blow. Others were to follow.

## CHAPTER SIX

# *The Navigators*

The great struggle which began with Copernicus and finally ended with Newton was a conflict in outlook. It affected science; it also affected religion, and general ideas about Man himself. It did not, of course, have much effect upon people as a whole. At this point in the story it seems, therefore, time to come back to the purely practical aspect, and to stress once again that astronomy can be useful as well as interesting.

I have concentrated mainly upon Western Europe because it was here that the most important advances were being made. Little was happening in China, and it is worth noting that Russia lagged behind in accepting the new ideas. In the New World, the Maya and the Inca tribes were no mean observers, and much could be written about them; but the practical work was European, and, during the seventeenth and eighteenth centuries, largely British.

One problem which had always been very much to the fore was that of navigation. Britain, as a seafaring nation, was deeply concerned, and it was a depressing fact that sailors who stayed out of sight of land for long periods were apt to become completely and sometimes permanently lost. What they wanted to do was to check upon their latitude and longitude, after which the available

> Science is nothing but trained and organized common sense, differing from the latter, only as a veteran may differ from the raw recruit: and its methods differ from those of common sense only as far as the guardsman's cut and thrust differ from the manner in which a savage wields his club.
>
> T. H. HUXLEY

HUDSONS BAY
TERRA DE LABORADOR OR NOVA BRITANNIA
NORTH AME
RICA
CANADA NEW FRANCE
NOVA SCOTIA
NEW ENGLAND
NEWYORK
PENSYLVANIA
MARYLAND
VIRGINIA
CAROLINA
FLORIDA
GOLFO de MEXICO
BAHAMA ISLES
HONDURAS
CARIBBE ISLANDS
S.t MARTHA
VENEZUELA
GUIANA
SOUTH
AME
RICA
North Cape
WILD
BRASILE
PERU
CHILI
PARAGUAY
PATA GO NIA
TERRA DEL FUEGO
C. Horn
THE PACI ICK SEA
West Variation
THE WESTERN OCEAN
AZORES
WESTERN ISLES
Tropick of Cancer
The Line of no Variation
East Variation
The Equinoctiall
CAPE DE VERDE ISLES
CANARY ISLES
NORWAY
THE GERMAN SEA
HOLLAND
FLANDERS
FRANCE
E RO
BAY OF BISCAY
SPAIN
MEDITERRANEAN
BARBARY
GUALATA
ARGUIN
AFRI
GUINEA
The Meridian of London
Tropick of Capricorn
East Variation
West Variation
THE SOUTHERN OCEAN
THE ICEY SEA
DEGREES of Variation
EAST WEST
The Curve Lines which are drawn over the Seas in this Chart do shew at one View all the places where the Variation of the Compass is the same. The Numbers to them shew how many degrees the Needle declines either Eastwards or Westwards from the true North; and the Double Line passing near Bermudas and the Cape de Virde Isles is that where the Needle stands true, without Variation
A New and Correct CHART Shewing the VARIATIONS of the COMPASS in the WESTERN & SOUTHERN OCEANS as Observed in ye Year 1700 by his Ma.ties Command by Edm. Halley
Sold by R. Mount and T. Page on Tower Hill London
Majestati semper Augustae GULIELMI III D. MAGNÆ BRITANNIÆ FR. Regis Invictissimi Tabula haec Hydrographica VARIATIONUM MAGNETICARUM Devotissime Consecratur a subdito Humillimo Edm. Halley

charts (drawn up by astronomical methods, of course) would give them all the information they needed. Latitude was no problem. All that had to be done was to measure the apparent height of the Pole Star above the horizon, because this height is always equal to the latitude of the observer (or, to be precise, within a single degree of it; the Pole Star is not exactly at the pole of the sky). It is true that our Pole Star never rises from places south of the equator, but there were no major difficulties. Longitude-finding was a very different matter, and it was this which caused all the trouble.

Various Governments offered large rewards for anyone who could solve the problem of longitude-finding at sea. Unfortunately, the ideas put forward were unworkable, and it was only in Newton's time that the first reasonable suggestions were made. These were based on the fact that the Moon moves comparatively quickly against the background of stars, and can therefore be used as a sort of clock-hand. Local time depends on one's position, and so it seemed that the Moon could be put to good use.

Two things had to be known: the accurate positions of the stars, which did not change appreciably, and the movements of the Moon. The whole matter was brought to the attention of King Charles II, who was highly sympathetic to science. It was pointed out that the best available star catalogue—Tycho Brahe's—was still not good enough to satisfy the navigators; it had been drawn up before the invention of the telescope, so that Tycho had had to depend upon naked-eye measurements. Accordingly, Charles ordered that a new observatory should be set up, and that a fresh star catalogue should be compiled specially for the use of British seamen. As official astronomer he appointed the Rev. John Flamsteed, who was

Edmond Halley

Halley's map of the Atlantic, the first published map to show lines of equal magnetic variation

an excellent observer even though he did quarrel with Newton and almost all his other contemporaries.

Greenwich Observatory was founded in 1675, and Flamsteed was given the salary of £100 per year—out of which he had to provide all his own scientific instruments! The catalogue took him many years, but at last it was completed, and it was certainly a great improvement upon Tycho's. Flamsteed was succeeded at Greenwich by Edmond Halley, who made a long series of observations of the Moon. Halley, incidentally, was also an explorer—or, at least, he went on long voyages in order to find out exactly how the compass needle behaves in various parts of the world. At one stage he even went far enough south to meet Antarctic icebergs. In 1702 he published his results on what we now call magnetic variation, and navigators found them remarkably useful.

Though the "lunar method" of longitude-finding was sound in theory, it was difficult in practice, and something even better was needed. The problem was solved by John Harrison, son of a Yorkshire carpenter, who invented the chronometer—that is to say, a time-keeper which would run for weeks or even months without losing or gaining more than a few seconds. This meant that seamen would always be able to find out Greenwich time; all they had to do was to look at the chronometer. Local time could easily be found by observation of the Sun and the stars; and comparison of the two times would give the required longitude.

The important point here is that Greenwich Observatory was set up not for "pure science", but for a very practical purpose indeed. Ever since then it has been regarded as the timekeeping centre of the world, and all nations take as their standard Greenwich Mean Time—that is to say the local time at the Observatory. In 1767 Nevil Maskelyne, at Greenwich, produced the first issue of the *Nautical Almanac*, which gave all the information needed for navigational purposes, and which has been published yearly from that time onward.

Originally, each country had its own "time standard". France worked according to the local time at Paris; Germany from Berlin, and so on. This meant that the map-making situation was confused, and it was clearly wise to adopt one "prime meridian" to be used by all nations. At an international conference in 1884 it was agreed that since Greenwich had taken the lead, Greenwich Time should be adopted. The only dissentients were, not unexpectedly, France and Ireland—but before long they, too, followed the general pattern.

There is no need to stress the value of astronomy in map-making and navigation. It had been realized in Greek times, perhaps even before; but as transport became more and more rapid, the world's leaders, both political and scientific, were forced to realize that standardization was essential. Without astronomy, it could never have been achieved.

Nowadays there are no large telescopes in use at the old observatory at Greenwich Park (though one should be in action there again by the end of 1973). Greenwich itself is no longer a village; it has become part of London, and the artificial lights and the atmospheric pollution make observing difficult. In our own time the main instruments have been moved to the clearer skies of Herstmonceux, in Sussex, and the original observatory has been turned into a museum. Go there, and you can still see the instruments which played so important a role many years ago.

Modern navigation is very complicated; radar

is the only one of the many methods which could not have been forecast in the early days of Greenwich. Clocks, too, are very different from the time-keepers used by Flamsteed, Halley and even Harrison. But when we come down to fundamentals, it is astronomy which is the key; and surely nobody could ever seriously claim that astronomers had no influence upon everyday life.

CHAPTER SEVEN

# *The Widening Outlook*

The growth of knowledge tends to take place in jerks. There was a major jerk of this kind during the last part of the seventeenth century, due largely to Newton but also to other brilliant men of the time—Flamsteed, for instance, and Halley. Then came a period of steady but less spectacular progress so far as astronomy was concerned. Telescopes were improved, and men could look further and further out into the universe; the more they probed, the less important Man seemed to become. There could no longer be any serious doubt that the Sun was a star, and that the Earth and other planets were merely members of the solar family. The old idea of the stars being points fastened to a crystal sphere looked very old-fashioned indeed.

It was around this time, too, that people in general began to think about the universe and their place in it. More people could read and write, and books were becoming much easier to get. The main effect was probably on religion; though as yet the influence was slight, it was increasing noticeably. For instance, what about the creation of the Earth? The straightforward Old Testament idea no longer satisfied everyone, and it was becoming clear that the history of our world extended backward well beyond Archbishop

William Herschel. This is an engraving after a pastel portrait by John Russel. Herschel is shown holding a diagram of Uranus and its satellites

Ussher's 4004 BC.

Various thinkers began to put forward ideas about the arrangement of the stars in space, and toward the end of the century the French astronomer Laplace proposed a theory to account for the origin of the Earth. According to Laplace, the Solar System began as a cloud of gas, which shrank steadily under the pull of gravitation. As it shrank, rings of gaseous material were left behind, and each ring condensed into a planet. Scientists in general were favourable to this "Nebular Hypothesis," as it was called, though some sections of the Church were not.

The next major steps were taken by a Hanoverian musician named William Herschel (originally Wilhelm), who spent most of his life in England and became the greatest observer of his time—perhaps of all time. From 1772 onward Herschel built large telescopes, and used them wisely. His reputation was made nine years later, when during one of his surveys of the night sky he discovered an object which did not seem to be a star. True, he did not at once realize its importance; but it moved slowly against the background of real stars, and before long it was found to be a new planet. We call it Uranus. It is just visible with the naked eye, but it is at the limit of vision, and the ancients could hardly have been expected to notice it.

This was another blow at dogma. Seven was the mystical number of astrology, and it had always been supposed that there could be only seven principal bodies in the Solar System: the Sun, the Moon, and five planets (Mercury, Venus, Mars, Jupiter and Saturn). Uranus did not fit into this picture at all, but its existence could not be denied.

Herschel's discovery altered his whole life. He gave up music as a career, and a modest pension from King George III allowed him to concentrate

Herschel's 40-foot Telescope

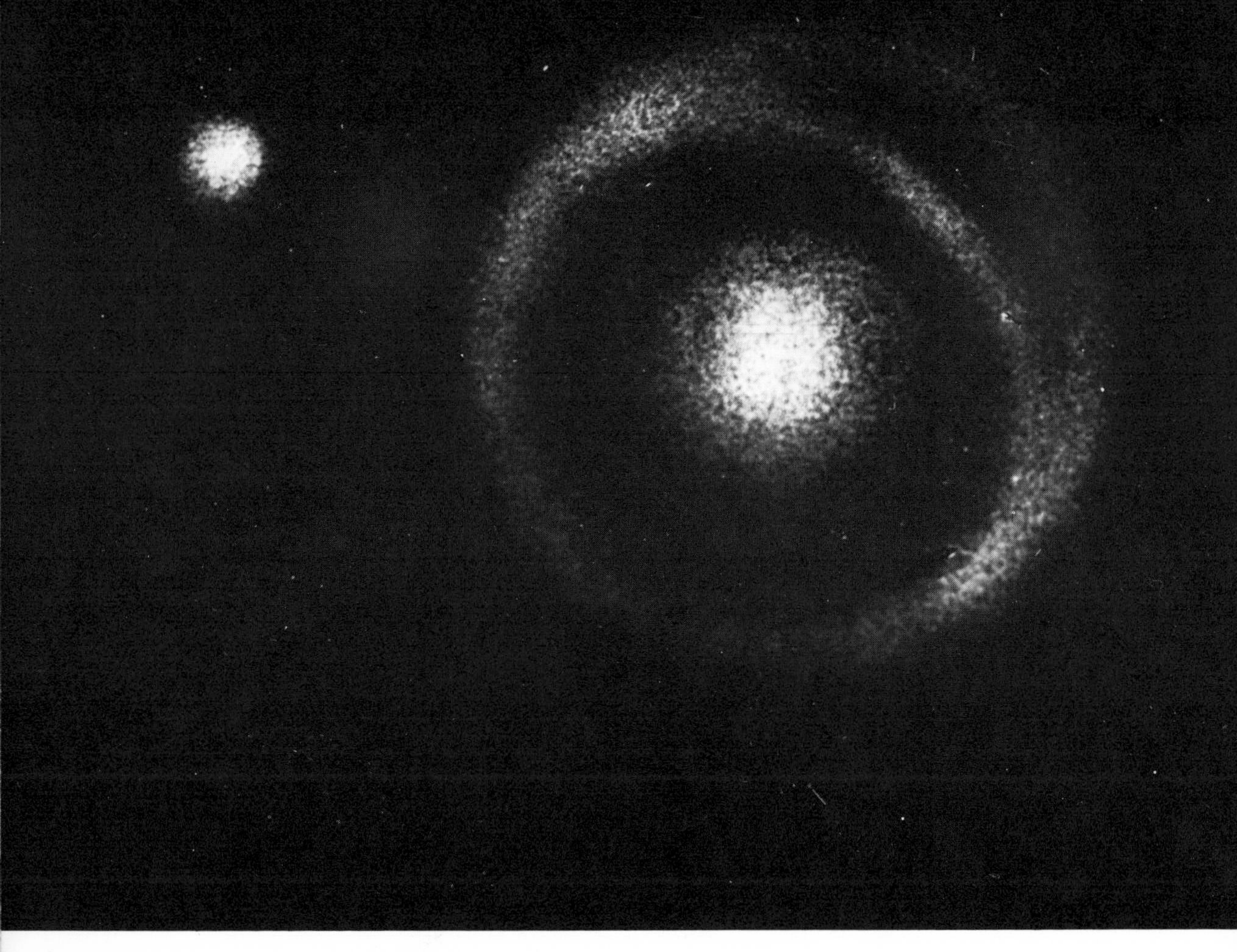

A drawing of nebulae by Herschel. This shows a very great advance over the work of earlier astronomers

upon astronomy. What he set out to do was to find out the shape of our star-system or Galaxy, and he spent countless hours at his telescopes, counting stars and doing his best to decide how they were distributed in space. Finally he came to the conclusion that the Galaxy was a somewhat flattened system, or—to use his own description—a "cloven grindstone"; less romantically, it may be compared with two fried eggs clapped together back to back. Herschel believed the Sun to lie near the middle, and this explained the appearance of the Milky Way, that lovely band of light which stretches across the sky and which Galileo had found to be made up of faint stars. Look along the main plane of a flattened system, and you will see many stars almost in the same direction. Herschel wrote, quite correctly, that the stars in the Milky Way were not really crowded together; they only seemed to be so.

The modern view of the Galaxy is not so very different from Herschel's, though we now know that instead of being central the Solar System lies well out toward one edge. And yet in some ways the great observer was anything but modern in his outlook. He was quite convinced that all the bodies in the sky were inhabited; he regarded the existence of Moon-men as "an absolute certainty", and he even thought that men might live in a pleasant, cool zone beneath the hot surface of the Sun.

It would take a long time to list all Herschel's

Herschel's view of the shape of the Galaxy (above) compared with its shape according to modern theory

discoveries. In particular he studied the misty patches which we call star-clusters and nebulae, and he wondered whether some of these nebulae might be independent star-systems far beyond our own. Unfortunately he had no means of proving it, because one thing he failed to do was to measure the distance of a star. The separation between the Earth and the Sun was reasonably well known (the modern value is just under 93,000,000 miles), and the stars were obviously much more remote, but that was as much as could be said.

Herschel tackled the problem in a typically sound manner. He reasoned that a comparatively nearby star would shift in apparent position during the year, relative to the background of more distant stars, simply because the Earth describes a wide orbit round the Sun. The diagram shows what is meant. In January, our nearby star will be seen in the position shown; six months later, when the Earth has moved round to the far side of its orbit, the star will appear in a slightly different position. Though the diagram has had to be drawn wildly out of scale, there is nothing wrong with the principle. The apparent shift in position is known as the star's parallax.

Parallax. The nearby star alters its apparent position as seen from opposite sides of the Earth's orbit (A and B)

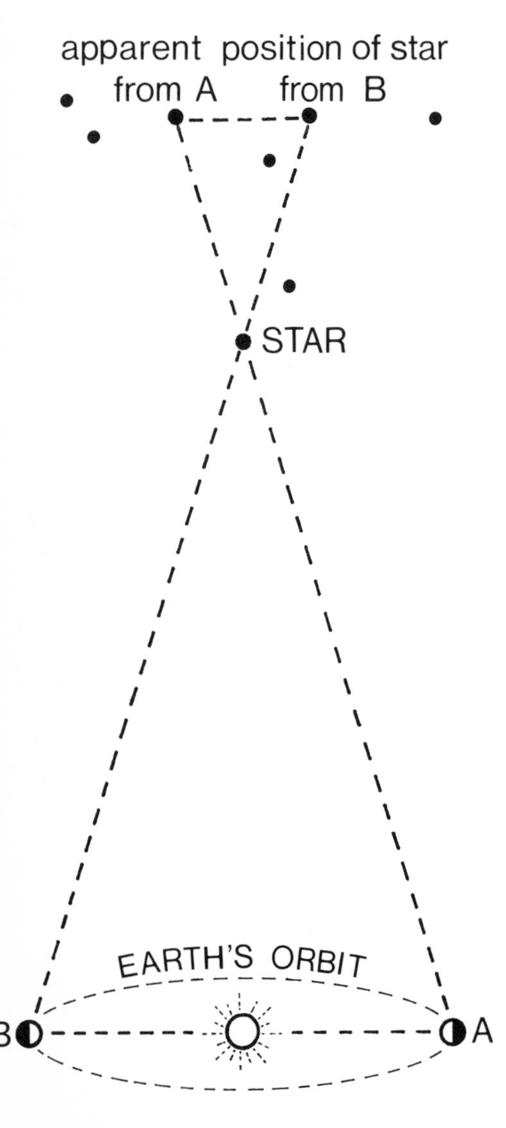


Herschel was unsuccessful because the parallax shifts are very small, and his measuring instruments were not sensitive enough to detect them, but in 1838—sixteen years after Herschel's death—the German astronomer F. W. Bessel was able to measure the parallax of a dim star known by its catalogue number of 61 Cygni. The distance proved to be approximately 60 million million miles, or 11 light-years.

The term "light-year" needs explaining, because it is so important. Much earlier, in Newton's lifetime, a Danish astronomer named Rømer had found that light does not travel instantaneously; it moves at the staggering rate of

A cartoon published in Punch in 1861—a contemporary, though inaccurate, view of Darwin's theory

186,000 miles per second. In one year, then, it will cover rather less than six million million miles (actually about 5,880,000,000,000 miles), and this distance is the astronomical light-year; note that it is a measure not of time, but of space.

Bessel's triumph went far toward putting the universe in proper perspective. Since most of the stars had parallaxes much smaller than that of 61 Cygni, they must be further away, and it followed that many of them must be far more luminous than the Sun. There was another consequence, too. If light took 11 years to reach us from 61 Cygni, then we must always see the star not as it is at the moment of observation, but as it used to be 11 years earlier. Our view of the universe is bound to be out of date. Nowadays this concept has become almost frightening. Modern telescopes can show us systems so remote that we see them as they used to be even before our world came into existence.

If the universe were on so vast a scale, then surely it must also have a tremendous time-scale? The "creation" was put back not to thousands of years, but to millions. Orthodox religion could not hope to argue against the growing mass of evidence, and the only escape-route was to claim that although the Earth was very ancient, Man had been created much more recently by a special act of God. Even this was challenged twenty years later. In 1859 Charles Darwin published his work on the theory of evolution, and sparked off one of the most bitter battles of scientific history; it was just as violent as the "Copernican revolution," even though it led to no public burnings in Rome.

Darwin never claimed that men are descended from monkeys. What he said, in effect, was that men, monkeys and apes have a common ancestry, which is by no means the same thing. What really

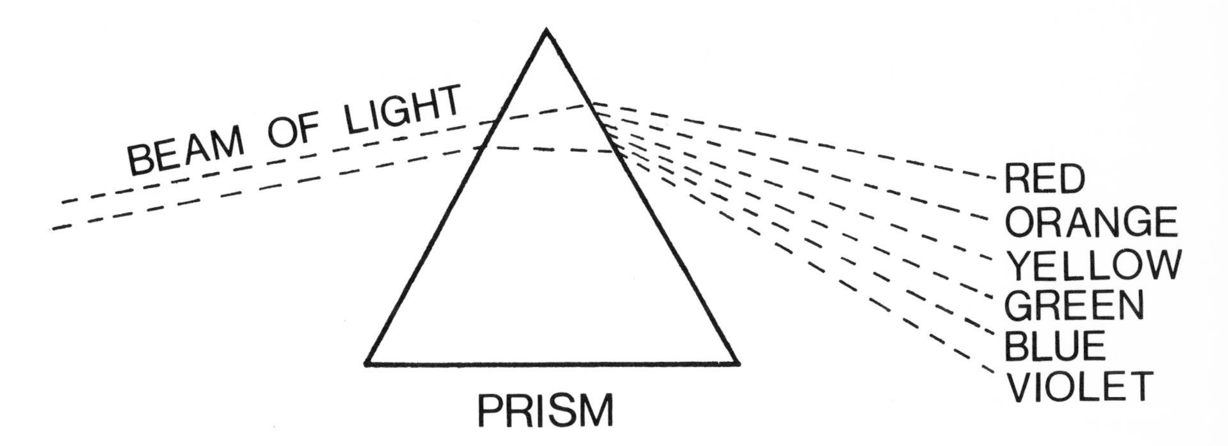


Production of a spectrum. The beam of light passes through the prism, and is spread out into a rainbow, with red at the long-wavelength end and violet at the short-wavelength end

angered his opponents was the suggestion that there is any connection at all between a man and what they called an "animal." If it were true, it would finally disprove the idea of God bringing mankind into existence at one definite moment in time, and it would also mean that the Biblical account could no longer be taken literally.

The link between Darwinism and astronomy is much closer than might be thought. The less intelligent Churchmen examined both, and liked neither; it was assumed that science had become irreligious. The argument was no longer confined to specialists. Ordinary people joined in—and, to some extent, they still do. The "Fundamentalist" who believes every word of the Bible to be literally true is uncommon today, but he still exists.

Meanwhile, there had been striking developments in other ways. As a starting-point we may take a statement made in 1830 by a philosopher named Auguste Comte. Comte wrote that there were some things which would always remain unknown, and as an example he gave what we may call the chemistry of the stars. Comte could not believe that we would ever learn what materials would be found in the stars; but the key to the problem had already been found. It was due originally to Sir Isaac Newton, who had passed sunlight through a specially-shaped piece of glass known as a prism, and had spread the light out into a spectrum or band of colours, from red at one end through orange, yellow, green and blue down to violet. Newton never took these particular experiments much further (he had other things to do!) but he had laid the foundations of the science we now call spectroscopy.

Just as a telescope collects light, so a spectroscope splits it up. In the early part of the nineteenth century a young German optician named Fraunhofer repeated Newton's experiments, and extended them; he found that the spectrum of sunlight was extremely complicated, and that the band of colours was crossed by permanent dark lines which are still sometimes called Fraunhofer lines. Later still—at about the time when Darwin's theories burst upon the world—another German, Gustav Kirchhoff, was able to give an explanation. He found that by studying the spectrum of a beam of light, whether from the Sun or from anything else, it was possible to learn a great deal about the nature of the material sending out the light. For instance, the spectrum of light emitted by hydrogen gas has its own particular trade-mark, and the same trade-mark is found when we look at the spectrum of the Sun. Therefore, the Sun contains hydrogen. The stars also show spectra of the same basic type, and we can find out the materials existing in them too. Comte's sweeping statement could not possibly have been more wrong.

The most important point of this work was that it linked astronomy with physics and chemistry—and this link has grown stronger and stronger over the years, until today it is impossible to tell just where astronomy ends and physics and chemistry begin. The two are different branches of the same science, just as arithmetic and algebra are two branches of the science of mathematics. Up to that

A cluster of galaxies in Hercules. This gives some idea of the possibilities of observation provided by the 200-inch Hale telescope

The Andromeda Galaxy. This is also shown in the frontispiece

time astronomy had been something quite apart, even though it had been so important in time-keeping and navigation. The spectroscope introduced an entirely new era.

It is not my aim here to give anything like a detailed account of the advances in astronomy during the last part of the nineteenth century and the first part of our own, but a little must be said, because it is so important when we come to consider the main effects upon human thought. Photography played a major part (how many people know that the very word "photography" was first used by an astronomer—Sir John Herschel, son of Sir William) and by 1900 photographic methods were well on the way to taking over from actual "star-gazing" through the eye-end of a telescope. Larger and larger telescopes were built, and it is interesting to note that they were privately financed. George Ellery Hale, an American astronomer, was able to persuade friendly millionaires to provide the money for a whole series of giant instruments, ending with the colossal 200-inch reflector at Palomar in California—though unfortunately the Hale telescope, as it is now known, was not completed until 1948, after Hale himself had died. It was one of these telescopes, the 100-inch reflector at Mount Wilson, which led to the discovery that the starry nebulae are indeed independent galaxies.

The work was carried out by using some remarkably convenient stars known as Cepheid variables, which brighten and fade with clockwork regularity over periods of a few days. It had already been found that the real luminosity of a Cepheid depends upon its period of variation; and once the luminosity is known, the distance can be worked out. The procedure is straightforward in theory, though difficult in practice. Using the 100-inch, Edwin Hubble found Cepheids in the Andromeda

Spiral. At once he was able to show that they lay far beyond the edge of our Galaxy, and one of astronomy's greatest arguments had been cleared up. We now know that the Spiral is so remote that its light takes over two million years to reach us. Even so, it is one of the closest of the outer systems.

Hubble's original estimate was too small, because there was an error in the Cepheid scale, and it was believed that the Andromeda Spiral must be much smaller than our Galaxy. Then, in the 1950s, the distance-scale was revised, and astronomers realized that far from being junior to our system the Andromeda Spiral is one and a half times as large. Once more we had been "cut down to size," and our last illusions of true importance were shattered. In ancient times it had been thought that the Earth must be supreme. When the Earth was found to be a planet moving round the Sun, many people claimed that the Sun, at least, was exceptional. It in turn became an ordinary star; then the Galaxy itself became an ordinary galaxy. In the universe as a whole, the Earth—and Man with it—had become sub-microscopic.

Hubble's discovery put the whole matter into a different perspective. All the spiral nebulae, and all the starry nebulae which were not spiral, came to be classed as separate systems; moreover, spectroscopic work showed that all except a few members of our own particular galaxy-group were racing away from us at high velocities. This did not mean that our Galaxy is particularly unpopular. Each group of systems is receding from each other group, and the universe is in a state of expansion.

Ask why the universe is spreading out, and the honest astronomer will admit that he does not know. Neither can we tell whether the expansion will go on indefinitely, and we cannot be sure whether or not "space" is endless. We are equally in the dark about the origin of the universe—a point to which I will return later.

Meanwhile, investigations about the nature of the stars had been going on. New instruments and new techniques altered many of the old-established ideas. For instance, a star such as the Sun is not burning; it is shining because of nuclear processes going on inside it, and it is losing mass steadily. Each second of time, the Sun, which is quite a mild star by stellar standards, is losing four million tons. In other words, it is changing its material into radiation, and this means that it cannot go on shining for ever.

The basic "fuel" is hydrogen, the light gas which is more plentiful than any other substance in the universe. Deep inside a normal star, where the pressure is tremendous and the temperature rises to millions of degrees, the hydrogen is being changed into another substance, helium, with the release of energy and loss of mass. Again we have a straightforward idea which is very complicated indeed when studied more closely, and it was only in the years immediately before the last war that astronomers found the main clues to the whole problem.

The point here is that the problem was as much concerned with physics and chemistry as with astronomy. Nuclear processes keep the Sun shining —and it is nuclear processes which produce bombs such as those which fell on Hiroshima and Nagasaki in 1945, and which are now stored by the great world powers in quantities sufficient to wipe out all mankind. It has been said, with truth, that the stars are Nature's greatest physical laboratories. Studies of them have made immense advances in knowledge possible. How we use these advances is a social problem, not a scientific one, and, of course, nuclear power has not been

The most important precursor of today's radio telescopes was Karl Jansky's directional radio aerial system, shown in this illustration

used solely for destruction. There may well come a time when our natural fuels, such as coal, become exhausted. If and when this happens, humanity must depend on peaceful adaptations of nuclear power, and already an encouraging start has been made. In this, the stars have certainly helped us.

Another close connection is with radio, and since the early 1930s it has been known that radio waves are coming from the sky. There is no suggestion that they are artificial; they are as natural as the familiar light-waves, and they too are classed as what we call electromagnetic vibrations. Light may be regarded as a wave-motion, and the colour of the light depends on its wavelength—that is to say, the distance between two successive wave-crests. Even with red light the wavelength is very short, and amounts to a tiny fraction of a millimetre. If the radiation has a wavelength longer than that of red light, it cannot be seen, because it does not affect our eyes, but it can be detected in other ways; and with longer and longer wavelengths we come eventually to the radio range.

The pioneer work in what we now call radio astronomy was carried out by an engineer named Karl Jansky, working in the United States. Amazingly, it caused almost no interest at the time, but since the war it has become of fundamental importance, and indeed the war had something to do with it. British workers found that some of their electronic devices were being "jammed," and at first it was thought that the interference came from Germany. Yet the Germans were not concerned; the trouble came from the Sun, which sends out long-wavelength radiations as well as visible light.

Today the vast instruments known, rather misleadingly, as radio telescopes collect these long waves, and a remarkable amount has been learned

Wavelength explained

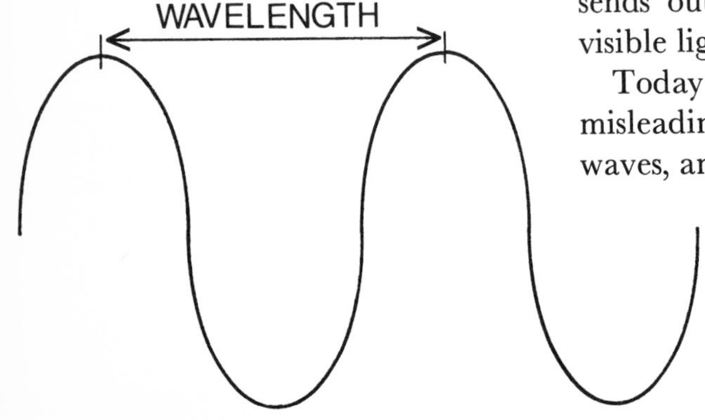

The Jodrell Bank 250 ft. Radio Telescope viewed from the Control Room

from them even though they cannot produce visible pictures of the objects being studied. Our knowledge of radio itself has been increased tremendously, and nobody can deny that this has an effect upon everyday life.

Oddly enough, it was found that most of the radio waves from the sky did not come from bright stars such as Sirius and Vega. For some years astronomers were badly puzzled, but at last they found out the origins of the radio waves. Some are due to patches of gas inside our own Galaxy; one powerful source is a hazy patch known as the Crab Nebula, which we know to be the remains of a star which exploded violently and literally blew itself to pieces. (The outburst was seen by Chinese astronomers in the year 1054, though the Crab Nebula is 6000 light-years from us, so that the explosion really happened well before civilization on Earth began.) However, most of the radio sources are due to independent galaxies at distances of millions, hundreds of millions, or even thousands of millions of light-years.

The 250 ft. steerable Mark I radio telescope at Jodrell Bank

Yet another shock came in 1963, with the identification of some strange objects known as quasars. They look rather like stars, but they are infinitely more dramatic. If our present estimates are correct, one quasar may shine as brilliantly as a hundred normal galaxies—and, remember, a galaxy may contain upward of a hundred thousand million suns! All kinds of suggestions have been made to explain this immense energy output, but as yet we have to admit that we do not know as much about the quasars as we would like.

Look at a quasar, or for that matter at an outer galaxy, and you are gazing through time as well as space. We see the Andromeda Spiral as it used to

> I will paint for man not only the visible universe but all that he can conceive of nature's immensity in the heart of the atom.
>
> PASCAL

> To strive, to seek, to find, and not to yield.
>
> *Ulysses*, TENNYSON

be over two million years ago, and few astronomers now doubt that the light now reaching us from the most remote quasars and galaxies started on its journey towards us even before the Earth existed as a separate body. The age of the Earth is known with fair accuracy, mainly through geological methods; it is around 4,700 million years, so that the Sun is presumably older than this, and the universe much older. This brings us back to the question of the creation—and, hence, to religion.

There has been a great deal of discussion lately about what is referred to as "the origin of the universe." According to one theory, the universe began at a definite moment, well over 10,000 million years ago; there was the sudden appearance of matter, which began to spread outward and condensed into galaxies, stars and planets. If this evolutionary theory is correct, the universe has a limited lifetime, and eventually it will die.

This rather depressing idea was challenged in the late 1940s by the so-called steady-state theory, which presented a completely different picture. In this, it was thought that the universe had always existed, and will exist forever; as old stars and galaxies die out, new ones are produced from material which is created out of nothingness. Of course, it was never suggested that a fresh star might appear at a moment's notice, or that a new Earth could be produced intact. The steady-state astronomers considered that fresh matter was created in the form of isolated atoms here and there, and that the rate of creation was too slow to be detectable. Unfortunately this made the theory impossible to check directly, but so many technical faults have been found in it that not many modern astronomers continue to support it. In its place there is the "cyclic" theory, according to which the universe alternately expands and contracts. At present the galaxies are racing away from each other; if the cyclic theory is right, they will eventually come together again, after which a new period of expansion will start. In fact, the universe is re-born every 60,000 million years or so.

Which theory is correct? We cannot be sure—but in fact none of them has any real connection with the *origin* of the universe. What we are discussing is the evolution of the universe, which is not the same thing. The one unchallengeable fact is that matter exists; and it must have come from somewhere. Just how it appeared in the first place is a total mystery.

The easy solution is to say simply that "God made it." This may be true, but it is no real scientific help! If we leave the problem there, we are really in no better a position than Archbishop Ussher used to be—and there is less excuse for us, because we have much more technical knowledge than Ussher had.

We must admit that our brains are not advanced enough to tackle questions of this kind. If the universe began at a definite moment, we are entitled to ask "Well, what happened before that?" And if the universe has always existed, we have to try to visualize a period of time which had no beginning. When we consider space, the situation is no easier. If space is limited, then what is outside it? A mathematical approach is the only possible one, but to put the problem into plain English is a hopeless task.

Because the Biblical account of the creation of the world is so far removed from science, it has been widely supposed that astronomers are irreligious. This is not necessarily true. As a class, astronomers—either professional or amateur—are no more religious but no more irreligious than anyone else. What they can do, better than most, is to appreciate the immensity of the universe and realize how small the Earth really is. Nobody

Has it ever occurred to anyone that space may eventually conquer man?
MARK MELTAIRE

If we continue at this leisurely pace, we will have to pass Russian customs when we land on the moon.
WERNHER VON BRAUN. London, 29th December 1959

has bettered the late Sir James Jeans' comment that the Earth is less important, cosmically speaking, than a single grain of sand in the entire Sahara Desert.

It may well be true that the knowledge gained by astronomers, and spread widely by means of books, radio and television, has made more people think carefully about the Earth's beginning and to see that there is more to it than a single act of God. But the Bible was never meant to be taken literally, as almost everyone now realizes. What astronomers and other scientists are doing is to search for fundamental truths, and there is nothing irreligious in this.

I hope that what has been said so far will be enough to show that there is nothing in the old claim that astronomy is an academic, impractical science. It is the basis of timekeeping; without it we could have no proper maps; navigation is astronomical; there are the closest possible links with optics, physics, chemistry and geology. Studies of the stars have helped immeasurably in our knowledge of the atom, and have opened up the way to the peaceful use of nuclear power. The mis-use of nuclear power for warfare is not the fault of the astronomer.

Quite apart from all this, there has been a great surge of interest in astronomy during the past couple of decades. People have looked more carefully at the sky, and in so doing have thought more carefully about the status of the Earth and its inhabitants. Part of the increased interest has been due to the space research programmes, but there are other reasons as well. The broadening of our outlook has been more rapid than at any period in human history except, perhaps, for those few years in the early seventeenth century when Galileo and his contemporaries were first turning their telescopes toward the sky.

CHAPTER EIGHT

# *Man in Space*

Not long before the outbreak of the last war I was attending a scientific meeting in London. I was in my teens, but already my interest in astronomy was strong, and I had actually been presenting a paper dealing with some observations I had been making of the Moon. During my address, I said that I expected men to land on the Moon before the year 2000. Later, during informal discussions over light refreshments, I could not help overhearing the comment of a world-famous astronomer: "These schoolboys have wild ideas, don't they?"

I reminded that astronomer of his remark only a few months ago—and he laughed. Of course, his attitude was very reasonable by the standards of 1939. Rockets were still weak and unreliable; the idea of travelling to the Moon did indeed seem schoolboyish and far-fetched. And yet my forecast was wrong by over thirty years. At that time I would never have dared to predict men on the Moon by 1969. (To my knowledge, the only Briton who made a correct forecast was Arthur Clarke.)

Reaching the Moon is not a modern concept. In Classical times Plutarch wrote a long, rambling essay in which he claimed that the Moon had mountains and valleys; Lucian of Samosata, in

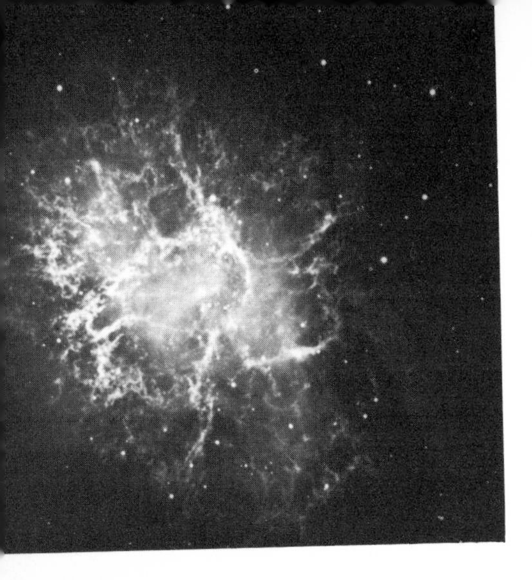

The Crab Nebula, in Taurus, Messier 1, photographed with the 200-inch Hale telescope

the second century AD, even wrote a story about a lunar voyage, though he did not intend it to be taken seriously. Much later, no less a person than Kepler wrote a strange book, the *Somnium* (Dream) in which he described a trip to the Moon, and went into great detail about the various forms of life to be found there. However, his suggested mode of travel—demon power—would not have appealed to modern astronauts; and neither would Jules Verne's idea of a space-gun capable of hurling a passenger-carrying projectile moonward at a starting speed of 7 miles per second (25,000 mph or thereabouts).

Jules Verne's famous novel *From the Earth to the Moon* appeared in 1865, and was an instant success; so was its sequel, *Round the Moon*, which was published a few years later. Verne was not a scientist, but he believed in checking his facts as carefully as he could, and the details given in his book sound highly convincing. Actually, the space-gun method cannot be used, partly because a projectile moving through the lower atmosphere at such a speed would be destroyed by friction and partly because the shock of starting would turn any luckless occupant into jelly. Moreover, the trip would be a one-way affair only, even if it could be made practicable.

Verne's story was popular because it was well-written, exciting and revolutionary in outlook. (It is significant that today a crater on the Moon is named in his honour.) Yet no scientists of the time seriously believed that his method would work, and they could not think of anything better, so that the Moon seemed well out of reach. It was not a question of sheer distance. The Moon is less than a quarter of a million miles away, and this is less than ten times the distance round the Earth's equator. But while no man could fly as much as ten feet above the ground, it seemed rather

The Blast Off, from Verne's *From the Earth to the Moon*

pointless to think about flying to the Moon.

Following Verne's novel, the idea of a lunar flight was discussed by many story-tellers, but not by any qualified scientists. The real pioneer of modern space-flight was a Russian, Konstantin Tsiolkovskii, whose first scientific papers about it appeared just before the turn of the century—even though their impact on scientific thought was about as great as that of a feather landing on damp blotting-paper! It was only later, when real advances had been made in America, that Tsiolkovskii's work became known.

There is an interesting parallel here between the story of space-flight and that of flight in the air. At about the time that Tsiolkovskii's papers were coming out in an obscure Russian journal, Orville and Wilbur Wright were working away at their primitive flying machine. One of America's leading astronomers, Simon Newcomb, published a book in which he proved quite conclusively that no heavier-than-air machine could ever fly, and showed that the best pattern would be in the nature of a vehicle pulled along by "a multitude of birds". Scepticism about the aeroplane continued even after the Wrights had made their first flights.

Of course, there was a great difference between the cases of aviation and astronautics. The possibility of flight within the atmosphere could be demonstrated simply by doing it—and when the Wrights produced their machines and flew them, the sceptics were silenced. Unfortunately it was not nearly so simple to build and demonstrate a space-ship, and it goes without saying that no amateur team could have attempted it.

Tsiolkovskii never fired a rocket in his life, but he did realize that rocket power is the only source which can be used for travelling to the Moon. This is because conventional flying machines cannot operate in vacuum—and the

The rocket on the way to the Moon, from the same book

The Principle of the Rocket

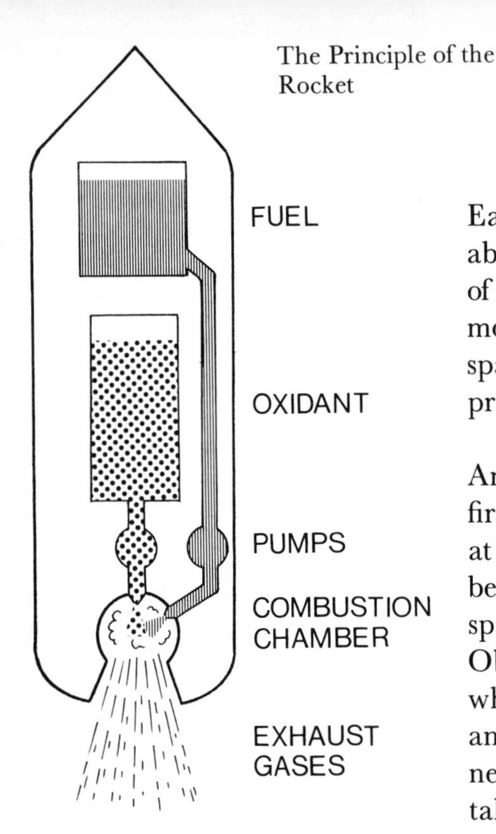


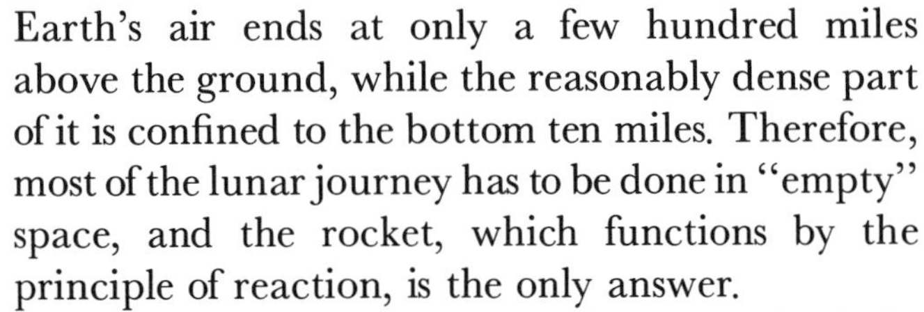

Earth's air ends at only a few hundred miles above the ground, while the reasonably dense part of it is confined to the bottom ten miles. Therefore, most of the lunar journey has to be done in "empty" space, and the rocket, which functions by the principle of reaction, is the only answer.

The first modern-type rocket was fired in America by Robert Goddard after the end of the first world war. It was a modest vehicle, travelling at a maximum speed of a mere 60 mph, but it may be regarded as the ancestor of today's Apollo space-craft. At around the same time Hermann Oberth, in Roumania, published a technical book which put astronautics on a truly scientific footing, and which became something of a bestseller. The next major steps came from Germany, where a talented team headed by men such as Wernher von Braun formed a "Society for Space Travel" and set to work designing rockets.

The German scientists were, in general, concerned only with the Moon, but unhappily the German Government was not. The Nazis came to power, and decided to turn the rocket research over to war preparations. At the base at Peenemünde, in the Baltic, a full-scale rocket base was set up, and it was here that von Braun and his colleagues produced the vehicle which became notorious as the V2. During the last months of the war, many V2s were fired at London and South England, doing a great deal of damage. Had the German rockets been ready a few years before they actually were, the result of the war might have been different—and civilization, in the true sense of the word, would have come to an abrupt even if a temporary end.

I cannot gloss over this aspect, because it gave the rocket an evil reputation; and echoes of the Peenemünde episode are heard even now, though von Braun himself has been so deeply involved in

The German V2 provided, during the Second World War, the first application of the rocket principle in a lethal weapon

the American space programme and has long been regarded as a highly respectable citizen of the United States. (This is quite logical. Von Braun made no secret of his interests, and at one stage during the war he was actually arrested on a charge of being too much concerned with space-flight and too little concerned with war weapons.) Moreover, it would be wrong to deny that there is no connection between military projects and space projects, because both use rockets. It is also true that had there been no war, the first lunar landing would not have been carried out nearly as early as 1969, and it would still be in the planning stage today.

Arguments of this kind have been used by opponents of the space programme, and they are not unfounded, but again the problems are social rather than scientific; and there are almost no scientific inventions which have not been misused at some time or other. The aircraft is a classic case. The machine which carries passengers from London to New York works on the same principle as the machine which is capable of dropping an atom bomb, but so far as I know there are no responsible people who have seriously suggested banning the manufacture of all aircraft.

At the end of the war, the idea of reaching the Moon still sounded rather far-fetched, and the growing Interplanetary Societies were not taken seriously. Quite apart from the technical difficulties of designing a suitable rocket, it was claimed that the human body could never stand up to conditions in space. But as the years went by, the "bogeys" were laid one by one. Man-made moons or artificial satellites were planned, and then launched; in my view the beginning of the Space Age dates from 4th October 1957, when the Russians sent up their first satellite, Sputnik I. Two years later, unmanned rockets went round

The first official picture of the first Russian Satellite, Sputnik I, in 1957

Yuri Gagarin, the first man in space

the Moon, and sent back photographs of that part of the lunar surface which is always turned away from the Earth and which we can therefore never see. In April 1961 Yuri Gagarin made the first space-flight, completing a full circuit of the Earth before landing safely back on terra firma; he was quite unharmed, and (as he told me some time later) had found the flight "pleasant and exciting." More unmanned satellites and more manned flights followed, and the climax came in July 1969 when Astronauts Neil Armstrong and Edwin Aldrin stepped out on to the rocks of the Moon. Terrestrial isolationism was at an end. By now, automatic rocket probes have landed gently on the furnace-hot surface of Venus; close-range pictures have been obtained of the craters and valleys of Mars, and a probe is on its way to Jupiter.

The sceptics have been silenced, only to be replaced by the protesters—who are remarkably vocal, and come from many walks of life. On the other hand, there are many people who are simply disinterested in the space programmes, and have become completely blasé about them. Nowadays a new unmanned Moon probe does not cause large, black headlines in the daily Press. If mentioned at all, it is liable to be on a back page; as a news item it certainly ranks well below the result of a football match.

Yet space research has already had tremendous effects upon ordinary life. The whole field of communications has been altered, and satellites in paths round the world are used as radio and television relays; without them it would be impossible to have direct television linkage over large distances, and as time goes by the communications satellites will become more and more important. Other satellites are used for mapping, for photographing wide areas in order to detect disease in forests or crops, and for geological prospecting. Yet others are concerned with meteorology, or weather science; and these may be taken as typical of satellites which are wholeheartedly beneficial to mankind.

Weather prediction is not merely a question of deciding whether to take one's macintosh when going on an afternoon drive to Bognor Regis. It is essential to farmers, particularly in areas subject to long droughts. Before the Space Age the forecasts were unreliable, largely because the weather experts had to take all their information from ground stations; they had to look at the atmosphere from underneath, and they could not hope to examine full-scale weather systems. The satellites altered all this. With a single photographic exposure it became possible to survey an entire weather system. Within a few years, our knowledge of the atmosphere had grown considerably, and forecasts today are much better than they were before Sputnik I—even though they still leave much to be desired!

Moreover, information sent back by satellites can give advance warning of dangerous storms building up over the ocean. Hundreds or even thousands of lives have already been saved in this way, and more could have been done if the satellite information had been used. The worst case was that of the appalling floods in what used to be East Pakistan and is now Bangladesh. The danger had been recognized, from satellite pictures, and the East Pakistani Government had been warned. They took no action whatsoever, and the death-roll was high; but it need not have been.

This is one instance of the practical value of space research. Many others could be given, but for the moment it will be enough to stress the connection with medical research, which is extremely close. The idea of a space hospital may sound far-fetched—but not nearly so wild as a flight to the Moon seemed in, say, 1930.

In view of this sort of research, it is not entirely easy to see what the protesters are protesting about. It is true that vast sums of money have been spent, both in America and in Russia, but to cancel the entire space programme would have no effect upon the outstanding social problems. It is also interesting to note that in 1969 the United States Government spent slightly less upon space research than it did upon military intelligence.

Edwin Aldrin, the second man to walk on the Moon

Undoubtedly the vast majority of thinking people realize the importance and the value of scientific progress—of which space research is a vital part. The main trouble up to now has been that political crises, occurring with monotonous regularity, have prevented real co-operation in space between the two pioneer nations, America and Russia. There has even been talk about a "space race" to the Moon. I have never believed in anything of the kind, and to me it seems clear that both programmes have been proceeding along their own individual lines; but full co-operation would be an immense help, and at last the signs are encouraging. It has been officially announced that within the next few years the Soviet and United States vehicles will be able to link together while in orbit round the Earth.

To many people today the novelty of space research has worn off. The changeover from amused scepticism to rather blasé acceptance has been amazingly rapid; it has taken less than two decades. Remember, too, that there are many people whose memories go back to the time when even aeroplanes were regarded as crazy dreams. I was not born until after that time, but at least I have talked with both the first airman (Orville Wright) and the first astronaut (Yuri Gagarin).

As yet, space developments have had only a limited effect upon people as a whole.

CHAPTER NINE

# *Man Beyond the Earth?*

Plaque, carried in Pioneer 10—the first probe to leave the Solar System

I doubt whether any problem has caused more argument than that of life on other worlds. Astronomers discuss it; so do chemists, biologists, and of course theologians. Originally there seemed to be nothing much to talk about. If the Bible (or, for that matter, the Koran) is taken literally, then Man must be all-important, and there is no room for another race of intelligent beings on Mars, Venus or anywhere else. But other people as well as Biblical Fundamentalists are sceptical about life beyond the Earth, and the whole question is a very difficult one.

The real trouble is that we do not know exactly how life on Earth began. The age of the world itself is, as we have noted, rather less than 5,000 million years, and it is fair to say that lowly forms of life appeared more than 3,000 million years ago. Over the ages these simple, single-celled creatures evolved into fishes, amphibians, mammals, and the special mammals which we call Men. Start with living matter, and the sequence can be traced through; but how did the first living matter appear? And was it pure chance?

Svante Arrhenius, a Swedish chemist who won a Nobel Prize early in the present century, suggested that life might have been brought to Earth by a meteorite. If a body came from space, bringing

Bright star, would I were
steadfast as thou art—
Not in lone splendour hung
aloft the night
And watching, with eternal
lids apart,
Like Nature's patient,
sleeping Eremite,
The morning waters at
their priestlike task
Of pure ablution round
earth's human shores.

*Sonnet to a bright Star,*
KEATS

The heavens themselves,
the planets, and this
centre
Observe degree, priority
and place,
Insisture, course,
proportion, season, form,
Office and custom, in all
line of order.

*Troilus and Cressida,*
SHAKESPEARE

living matter with it, then this living matter might survive, spread, and eventually produce you and me. Unfortunately this so-called "Panspermia" theory only replaces one difficulty by another, for we still have to explain how the living matter came into existence, and to transfer it from the Earth to a meteorite only makes the question still more difficult to answer. Much more recently there have been suggestions that organic material has been found on meteorites of a certain special kind, but the evidence is very shaky indeed.

The only way to obtain definite proof is to handle specimens of extra-terrestrial life. The Moon, as expected, has provided none. All the pieces of Moon-rock brought home by the American astronauts and the Russian automatic rockets have been completely sterile, and we are no longer in any doubt that the Moon has been lifeless all through its long history. (Even the quarantine regulations for spacemen coming home from the lunar surface have been cancelled.) The planet Venus has a surface temperature of approximately 900 degrees Fahrenheit, and a dense atmosphere made of carbon dioxide, which does not seem very promising. Of the remaining planets, Mercury has virtually no atmosphere, and all the giants (Jupiter and beyond) are too cold, quite apart from the fact that their surfaces are made of gas. Pluto, too, is hopelessly chilly. In the Solar System, then, our hopes are centred upon Mars.

Mars, further from the Sun than we are, has a cold climate, and a thin, carbon-dioxide atmosphere, but we cannot yet rule out the chance of some sort of life there. The famous dark markings, first seen as long ago as 1659, could be due to organic matter, though most people (including myself!) are less confident about it now than we used to be before the first successful Mars probe by-passed the planet in 1965. But we can certainly discount the idea of intelligent Martians, or even of small mammals, because the conditions are much too hostile. In the Solar System there is no advanced life, except on the Earth. If we want to contact other intelligent races, we must go beyond; and this involves crossing distances of millions of millions of miles.

One argument, often put forward, should be discussed here. The question is generally put as follows: "It is agreed that life of our own kind could not exist on, say, Mercury or Jupiter; but what is the objection to there being entirely alien life-forms, which could manage excellently without atmosphere or in a temperature of hundreds of degrees below zero?" This leads on to the idea of what science-fiction writers usually call BEMs, or Bug-Eyed Monsters. The best of all BEMs were created by H. G. Wells in his classic novel *The War of the Worlds*, but there have been plenty of others.

Let us admit, straight away, that nobody can prove that BEMs do not exist. So long as we have not solved the problem of the origin of life, it would be most unwise to be too definite. Yet although we are still very much in the dark about life itself, we know a great deal about living matter, and we know that the large, complicated atom-groups or molecules needed can be based on only one element: carbon. (One other element, silicon, cannot be entirely ruled out, but we have no evidence of silicon-based life anywhere.) Now, astronomers can show that the material making up a man, an earwig, a typewriter or a stone is composed of the same elements as those making up stars and galaxies millions of light-years away, and this is science rather than speculation. Our BEM would have to be made up of quite alien substances, and we have firm evidence that these

Hereafter, when they come
to model heaven
And calculate the stars, how
they will wield
The mighty frame how
build, unbuild, contrive,
To save appearances,
how gird the sphere
With centric and eccentric
scribbled o'er
Cycle and epicycle, orb in
orb.

MILTON

Science moves, but slowly, slowly, creeping on from point to point.

TENNYSON

From all I may be, or have
been before,
To mingle with the
Universe, and feel
What I can ne'er express,
yet cannot all conceal.

BYRON

substances do not exist.

Therefore, life—wherever it exists—must be based on carbon, and thus rules out intelligent beings on a world which does not have the right kind of environment. We need a reasonably constant temperature, the right kind of atmosphere, and plenty of water. Without all these essentials, life will not appear; and when conditions become unsuitable, life will die out.

This is sound science, and it is also logical. I repeat that I cannot prove the non-existence of alien life; but if it exists, then much of our modern science is wrong—for which there is no evidence whatsoever. All we can really do is to take what facts we have, and put the best possible interpretation on them. I can add little more, except that for the moment it seems sensible to relegate BEMs to the pages of science-fiction novels and to limit our discussion to life of the sort we can understand.

Before going on, something must be said about the flying saucer craze, mainly because much of it has a religious background (even though this religious link is not of the conventional type). Ever since the late 1940s there have been stories of strange space-craft which are keeping the Earth under close watch, and which periodically land here, so that the alien visitors can make a few contacts with selected Earthmen before flying off once more. According to the Saucer societies, some of the ships come from Venus, others from Mars and even Saturn. One band of enthusiasts even claims that Jesus Christ was a Venusian, and that the great Chinese philosopher Confucius came from Saturn. In general it is said that the flying saucers are friendly, and are doing their best to help us, though from time to time there are dark hints about visiting space-craft which are anything but well-meaning.

Of course, the idea that the Earth is the only inhabited planet in the Solar System is relatively new. A century and a half ago it was widely thought that other races might be fairly near at hand. As we have noted, Sir William Herschel was convinced that there were beings on the Moon, Mars and even inside the Sun; during the 1830s a famous newspaper hoax in America led thousands of people to believe that Sir John Herschel (son of Sir William) had used his powerful telescope to discover weird animals on the Moon; much later, from 1877, very eminent astronomers seriously thought that the so-called canals on the surface of Mars were artificial. But with all that the science of today has told us, the popular belief in flying saucers is really mysterious.

Perhaps the reason is that many people would like to believe in visits from Outer Space, and at least the saucer cult is an indication that more and more people are thinking hard about life beyond the Earth. It is a harmless belief, and the occasional flying saucer item on the news bulletins is a welcome change from the usual catalogue of strikes, violence and political squabbling.

More seriously, people are also thinking about the scientific possibilities of other intelligent beings. Everything depends upon there being suitable planets, and here our ideas have changed very much during the past few decades.

We may be confident that the planets were born between four and five thousand million years ago. A theory very popular just before the war, always linked with the name of Sir James Jeans, explained the origin of the Solar System quite simply as being due to the pull of a star which by-passed the Sun, drawing out a tongue of solar material which broke up into drops—each drop condensing into a planet. Now, it is known that the stars are widely spread-out in space, and relatively speaking space is much less crowded than the Royal Festival Hall would be if it contained nothing except for a couple of mosquitoes. A close approach between two stars must be very rare; and if the planets had been formed in such a way, our Solar System might well have been the only one in the Galaxy.

However, the mathematicians have attacked Jeans' theory so savagely that it has been more or less abandoned, and nowadays it is thought more likely that the planets were produced from a cloud of material which used to surround the Sun. Our Sun is a normal star, and there are many millions like it. If it has a system of planets, then why should not other suns have systems of the same kind? There seems no reason to think otherwise, and we have excellent indirect evidence that some of the nearer stars are indeed attended by invisible bodies which are probably planets.

Obviously this alters the whole situation. There are 100,000 million stars in our Galaxy; the world's largest telescopes can photograph at least a thousand million galaxies, and so the total number of stars which we know to exist is staggeringly great. To suppose that our Sun is unique in being accompanied by a habitable planet would indeed be the height of conceit.

The next question is just as important. If a planet is habitable, then will life automatically appear on it? Most scientists would say "yes;" some theologians would say "no." Mars may provide the answer. Nobody with any real knowledge believes in Martians, but there just may be lowly organic matter, and the soft-landing probes now being planned in America and Russia should tell us. If there is life of any sort on Mars, no matter how primitive, we shall have a clear indication that other worlds too can produce living things, and it will be reasonable to suppose that these life-forms will develop as far as their environment allows.

Consider a planet moving round a distant star, several tens of light-years from the Sun. If the planet is of about the same size as the Earth, and if its sun is about the same size and luminosity as our Sun; if the planet is at about 93,000,000 miles from the star, and if it has an oxygen-rich atmosphere and wide oceans—then it will be peopled by beings of the kind we would instantly class as "men"? It seems logical, though there is no proof.

This idea strikes at the roots of orthodox religion much more strongly than Copernicus or Galileo ever did. Instead of being the supreme race, Man on Earth may be very insignificant—like a single shrimp swimming in the sea off Selsey Bill. Note, however, that I say the idea is contrary to orthodox religion, and not to religion itself. Many scientists believe that although there must surely be many races living on many planets in many galaxies, there could well be one universal power embracing them all.

The gap between science and religion seems, indeed, to be much less marked than was thought. All that modern advances in knowledge have done is to show that we are not supreme, and there is nothing irreligious in this. Of course, sciences does oppose the older and more literal form of religion, but this was bound to be replaced in any case, and the change applies to all the accepted religions of the world—not only to Christianity. Certainly we do urgently need a code of belief and behaviour which will lead to a tolerant and decent civilization in which Governments are concerned with true progress rather than upon building nuclear bombs to drop upon their neighbours; and so far nobody can seriously claim that we have found it.

The widening of outlook may, then, be a vital step in our advancement. How far it will take us we do not yet know.

CHAPTER TEN

# *The Future*

In this book I have done my best to trace the changing outlook of mankind from the far-off days of the supreme Earth down to the present time, when we have just realized how unimportant we really are. What, then, of the years to come?

At a purely scientific level, there can be no doubt at all that astronomy, together with space research, will become more and more a part of daily life. Communications satellites will be developed until they will presumably make old-fashioned methods, such as undersea cables, quite obsolete. The "storm alert" system will be perfected, and we should be able to draw up a really reliable service of weather forecasting which will revolutionize world agriculture. In many other ways, too, the satellites will be pressed into service. The main danger is that they will be used—or, rather, misused—for military purposes, and we can only hope that the new suggestion of East–West collaboration in space will be brought about quickly.

So far as manned space-research is concerned, we must await the results of the Skylab orbital station which is now being planned. Man may or may not be able to tolerate long periods under conditions of weightlessness. If he can, then we may expect full-scale space-stations within the next decade, and among the many benefits of these will be the medical advances. If not, then admittedly we must wait until a solution is found. The obvious one is to build stations which spin round, so creating "substitute gravity" at their edges. There are very major practical difficulties here, and all space-planners hope that nothing of the kind will be necessary. What must be avoided at all costs is another tragedy similar to that of Soyuz II, when the three Russian cosmonauts were in excellent physical shape when leaving their orbital base but were dead by the time that they landed back on Earth.

One aspect of the space programme, too often overlooked, is that in the long run it may do much to bridge the political differences between nations. If, say, the Russians and the Americans have a combined team operating on a space-station (or, looking further ahead, on the Moon) there is a clear basis for real understanding, and it may even hold out the best possible hopes. This is not so far-fetched as it may sound, and it is much less unlikely now than it was in the early 1960s, when people in general were still thinking in terms of a race to the Moon. I am reminded, also, of the crisis which faced Apollo 13, the American craft which was crippled by an explosion on its outward journey to the lunar surface. The landing on the Moon was immediately given up, and everything was concentrated upon bringing the three astronauts back safely. Their progress was followed just as keenly, and with just as much concern, in the East as it was in the United States and Britain. For a brief period, until Lovell, Haise and Swigert touched down successfully in the ocean, the differences between the nations seemed to be forgotten. To me, at least, this was an indication that the apparently never-ending crises are confined to Governments and officials,

SKYLAB, the new orbital station which may make manned space

and people as a whole have no patience with them. Perhaps space research will show us the way to overcome them.

Children of 1972 accept the idea of flight to the Moon, just as the children of 1932 accepted the aircraft; both would have been wild flights of fancy to a child of 1832—or even 1872. Again we see how much our outlook has widened; and as we send our probes and our astronauts further into space, Man may become less preoccupied with his local quarrels. The signs are there, and they are not discouraging.

Much further ahead still, we come to the problem of contact with other intelligent beings—and I am well aware that this may never happen. There is no question of our being able to send rockets of present-day type as far as the stars; the time of travel would be impossibly long, and ideas of "deep-freezing" crew members, or building space-arks, are likely to remain fictional only. When an automatic probe was sent out toward Jupiter, in 1972, it was fitted with an identification plaque, because the vehicle will eventually leave the Solar System and there is always a chance that it will be picked up by some alien civilization; but the odds are many millions to one against! And we must admit that interstellar travel will need some technique which is, as yet, so far beyond our powers that we cannot even speculate profitably about it.

On the other hand, we come back to the logical idea that our civilization is only one of many, and is probably not very advanced. Elsewhere, on planets of other stars, there are almost certainly races which far outstrip us both technically and morally. We may picture worlds upon which war has long been outlawed, and where the main concentration has been on the conquest of disease. No doubt there are also worlds upon which a civilization has appeared, thrived for a time and then failed, by wiping itself out—as we on Earth are in real danger of doing today. But if we are to be visited, it can only be by a highly advanced race, and it is not likely to be hostile. This is one reason why the Bug-Eyed Monsters of fiction (from H. G. Wells downward) are so unlikely. There is no reason whatsoever to suppose that a being from another world will be either repulsive or unfriendly. If he (or she, or it) belongs to a race which has learned how to achieve interstellar travel, the reverse is likely to be the case.

My own view, for what it is worth, is that if contact is ever to be made with a civilization from another solar system, it will probably be by some method which does not involve actual material travel. To speak about thought-communication may sound wild today, but no wilder than, say, television would have done to Alfred the Great. Unfortunately our brains are not advanced enough for us to do more than speculate, and until we develop further there is not much that can be said.

The impact of contact with another race would—needless to say!—be quite devastating. All our pre-conceived ideas and all our prejudices would have to be swept aside, and our whole attitude toward the universe, toward life, and toward ourselves would be altered at once. Whether it will ever happen I do not know. I hope it will, but it may be delayed for a very long time even if it happens at all.

Further ahead still—so far ahead, indeed, that our imagination fails us—there must come a time when the Earth itself is in danger of destruction. Our Sun is a stable star, shining steadily; it will continue to do so for at least six thousand million years, and perhaps even longer. Yet it is using up its reserves, and eventually its supply of "fuel" will run low. When this time comes, the Sun will rearrange itself drastically, and there will be a period when it will send out about a hundred times as much radiation as it does now. It will turn into a red giant star, and the results on the nearer planets, including Earth, will be disastrous. Even if they survive, they will lose their atmospheres, and will become uninhabitable. Long before the Sun collapses into the state of a very small, feeble, super-dense star of the type known as a white dwarf, the story of life on Earth will have come to an end.

The danger will not come quickly; there will be plenty of warning, and humanity, if it survives, will have millions of years in which to prepare for the crisis. It may involve physical transfer to another world; there may be other solutions—we cannot tell. But if Man still inhabits the Earth at that remote epoch, we may be confident that he will have learned enough to save himself in one way or another. The end of life on our own planet need not mean the end of the human race.

But we have gone beyond the boundaries of normal speculation, and at present we are concerned with the next few centuries rather than the inconceivably remote future. Each year brings its new advances, its new enlightenment; scientific and social studies are coming closer together, not moving further apart; and in all this, the "watcher of the skies" plays a great part. We no longer worship the Sun or the Moon, and we no longer believe that the movements of the planets control our destinies, but Man is still an astronomer—just as he used to be in the days of the Pyramids, and as he will always be in the years ahead.

# *Date Chart*

**BC**

| | |
|---|---|
| 2890 | Egyptian period begins: King Menes. |
| 2613–2494 | Pyramids built. |
| 2800–1900 | Stonehenge built. |
| 1370 | Akhenaten's Sun religion. |
| 580 | Pythagoras speculates about the movements of planets and the form of the Earth. |
| 280 | Aristarchus speculates about the movement of the Earth round the Sun. |
| 270 | Eratosthenes measures the size of the Earth. |

**AD**

| | |
|---|---|
| 120–180 | Work of Ptolemy at Alexandria. |
| 1433 | Ulugh Beigh's great observatory at Samarkand. |
| 1543 | Publication of Copernicus' great book, showing that the Earth moves round the Sun. |
| 1576 | Tycho Brahe sets up his observatory at Hven. |
| 1600 | Martyrdom of Giordano Bruno. |
| 1609 | Telescopes first used in astronomy. Publication of Kepler's first two Laws of Planetary Motion. |
| 1633 | Trial of Galileo for heresy. |
| 1675 | Greenwich Observatory founded, for navigational purposes. |
| 1687 | Publication of Newton's work on gravitation. |
| 1767 | First issue of the *Nautical Almanac.* |
| 1781 | Herschel discovers Uranus. |
| 1786 | Herschel's theory of the shape of the Galaxy. |
| 1838 | First measurement of the distance of a star (Bessel). |

| | |
|---|---|
| 1840 | First astronomical photographs taken. |
| 1903 | Tsiolkovskii's first published work on astronautics. |
| 1917 | Completion of the great 100-inch telescope at Mount Wilson. |
| 1923 | Hubble proves that the galaxies are external systems. |
| 1931 | Jansky first picks up radio waves from the sky. |
| 1948 | Completion of the 200-inch Hale reflector. |
| 1957 | First artificial satellite (Sputnik I). |
| 1961 | First manned space-flight (Gagarin). |
| 1962 | First successful planetary probe (Mariner 2, to Venus). |
| 1963 | Discovery of quasars. |
| 1966 | First soft landing of an automatic probe on the Moon. |
| 1969 | First men on the Moon (Armstrong and Aldrin). |
| 1972 | Launching of the first probe designed to leave the Solar System (Pioneer 10, by-passing Jupiter). |
| 1973 (?) | First true space-station: Skylab. |

# *Glossary*

ASTEROID. Small planet less than 500 miles in diameter. Most of the asteroids keep to the region of the Solar System between the orbits of Mars and Jupiter.

ASTRONAUT. Space-man. This is the American term; the Russian equivalent is "cosmonaut."

CARBON DIOXIDE. Heavy gas, made up of carbon and oxygen; chemical formula $CO_2$. It makes up most of the dense atmosphere of Venus and the thin atmosphere of Mars.

CEPHEID VARIABLE. A star which changes its brightness regularly over a short period (usually a few days). The real luminosity of a Cepheid is linked with its period of variation, so that we have a convenient method of measuring its distance.

CHRONOMETER. An accurate timekeeper, suitable for being taken on board ship during a long voyage.

COMET. Member of the Solar System, made up of small particles (mainly ices) and thin gas. Most comets move round the Sun in very eccentric orbits.

CONSTELLATION. Group of stars. However, the stars in a constellation will be at very different distances from us, and are not genuinely associated.

COPERNICAN THEORY. The hypothesis that the Earth revolves round the Sun, and not *vice versa.*

EARTH. The third planet in order of distance from the Sun.

ECLIPSE, LUNAR. Eclipse of the Moon—caused when the Moon passes into the shadow of the Earth, and its supply of direct sunlight is temporarily cut off. A lunar eclipse may be either total or partial.

ECLIPSE, SOLAR. Eclipse of the Sun—caused when the Moon passes directly between the Earth and the Sun, thereby blotting out the Sun's bright disk. If the eclipse is total, the Sun's atmosphere (the *chromosphere* and *corona*) may be seen with the naked eye; but no total eclipse can last for as long as 8 minutes. If the eclipse is partial, the Sun's atmosphere cannot be seen with the naked eye.

EQUINOX, SPRING (First Point of Aries). The passage of the Sun across the equator of the sky, moving from south to north, about March 22. The position of the First Point of Aries is no longer in the constellation of Aries; precession has moved it into the adjacent constellation of Pisces.

FRAUNHOFER LINES. Dark (absorption) lines in the spectrum of the Sun. They are named in honour of J. Fraunhofer, who first studied them in detail.

GALAXIES. Independent stellar systems, far beyond our own.

GALAXY. The stellar system which contains our Sun. It includes about 100,000 million stars, as well as clusters, nebulae and various other types of objects. When we look along the main plane of the Galaxy, we see the luminous band which is known as the *Milky Way*.

HELIUM. The second lightest element. Under ordinary conditions it is a gas.

HOROSCOPE. An astrological chart. It is concerned with predicting the future by means of the apparent positions of the planets, and has no scientific basis.

HYDROGEN. The lightest element. Under ordinary conditions it is a gas, and it is by far the most plentiful element in the universe.

LATITUDE. The angular distance of a point on the Earth's surface north or south of the equator.

LONGITUDE. The angular distance of a point on the Earth's surface east or west of the Greenwich meridian.

LIGHT-YEAR. The distance travelled by a ray of light in one year. It amounts to approximately 5,880,000,000,000 (nearly six million million) miles, since light moves at 186,000 miles per second.

METEOR. A small particle which burns away in the Earth's upper air.

METEORITE. A larger body which lands on the Earth without being destroyed during its drop through the atmosphere. A meteorite is not merely a large meteor; it is probably more closely related to an asteroid. Meteors, meteorites and smaller particles in space are often known collectively as *meteoroids*.

MOON. The Earth's natural satellite. The term "moon," with a small m, is often (though misleadingly) used as a synonym for "satellite."

NEBULA. A cloud in space, made of small particles and tenuous gas.

NEBULAR HYPOTHESIS. An old theory of the formation of the Solar System, due to Laplace. It assumed that the planets were formed by rings of gas left behind as the original gas-cloud shrank. The Sun is taken to be the remnant of the cloud. In its original form, the theory is no longer accepted.

ORBIT. The path of a celestial body in space.

PARALLAX. This depends upon the apparent yearly shift in position of a distant astronomical object, due to the real movement of the Earth round the Sun.

PHASE. The apparent changes in shape of the Moon each month, from new (invisible) to full. The inferior planets, Mercury and Venus, also show phases, since they are closer to the Sun than we are.

PLANET. A non-luminous body, moving round the Sun and shining by reflected sunlight. The principal planets of the Solar System are Mercury, Venus, the Earth, Mars, Jupiter, Saturn, Uranus, Neptune and Pluto.

POLES, CELESTIAL. The positions in the sky indicated by the direction of the Earth's axis of rotation. The north celestial pole is marked approximately by the star Polaris, which is less than one degree from the actual pole. The south celestial pole is not marked by any bright star.

QUASAR. A very remote, highly luminous body, far beyond our Galaxy. The exact nature of quasars is still not known.

PRECESSION. The apparent shift in position of the Earth's axis, due to the gravitational pulls of other celestial bodies. It is responsible for the slow movement of the celestial poles.

PRIME MERIDIAN. The meridian of longitude which passes through Greenwich Observatory. By international agreement it marks the zero for longitude reckoning.

PTOLEMAIC THEORY. The old theory of the universe, according to which the Earth lay in the centre.

ROCKET. A vehicle which moves by means of the principle of reaction, and which can therefore function in vacuum. Most present-day rockets have chemical fuels; future rockets will certainly have nuclear fuel.

SAROS. A cycle of approximately 6,585 days. After one Saros the Earth, Sun and Moon return to almost the same position relative to each other. The Saros can therefore be used to predict eclipses, though not with real accuracy.

SATELLITE. A secondary body moving round a planet. (This is an oversimplification, but is approximately valid). The Earth has one natural satellite—the Moon; Jupiter has 12, Saturn 10, Uranus 5, and Neptune and Mars 2 each. Since 1957 many artificial satellites have been put into orbit round the Earth.

SKYLAB. The American space-station project, scheduled for 1973.

SOLAR SYSTEM. The system of the Sun. It contains one star (the Sun itself); the nine principal planets; the satellites, comets, meteoroids, and interplanetary débris.

SPECTROSCOPE. An instrument used for analyzing light.

SPUTNIK. A common nickname for "artificial satellite," since the first such vehicle was Russia's Sputnik I, launched on 4th October 1957.

STAR. A globe of incandescent gas, shining by its own light. Normal stars radiate by the conversion of hydrogen into helium, with steady loss of mass.

SUN. The star which lies at the centre of the Solar System.

SUPERNOVA. A vast explosion, in which a star destroys itself. It is thought that the end product of a supernova is a cloud of expanding gas, together with a very small, amazingly dense "stellar remnant" emitting radio waves and known as a *pulsar*.

TELESCOPE. Instrument for obtaining magnified views of distant objects, and for detecting very faint objects. Astronomical telescopes are of two main kinds. The *refractor* collects its light by means of a glass lens or objective, while the *reflector* uses a specially-shaped mirror.

ZODIAC. The belt round the sky in which the Sun, the Moon and the bright planets are always to be found.

# *For Further Reading*

Clarke, Arthur C. *The Promise of Space* (Hodder & Stoughton).

Hoskin, M. *William Herschel and the Construction of the Heavens* (Oldbourne Press).

Moore, Patrick. *The Amateur Astronomer: Space* (Both Lutterworth Press).
*The Sky at Night* (BBC).

Ronan, C. A. *Their Majestie's Astronomers* (Bodley Head).

Satterthwaite, G. E. *Encyclopedia of Astronomy* (Hamlyn).

Whitney, C. A. *The Discovery of our Galaxy* (Angus & Robertson).

(Periodicals) *Sky and Telescope.* Cambridge, Mass., U.S.A.
*Astronomy and Space.* David & Charles, Newton Abbot.

# *Index*